PROCEEDINGS OF SPIE

 SPIE—The International Society for Optical Engineering

Medical Imaging 1998

Image Perception

Harold L. Kundel, M.D.
Chair/Editor

25 February 1998
San Diego, California

Sponsored by
SPIE—The International Society for Optical Engineering

Cooperating Organizations
American Association of Physicists in Medicine
American Physiological Society
FDA Center for Devices and Radiological Health
IS&T—The Society for Imaging Science and Technology
National Electrical Manufacturers Association/Diagnostic Imaging
  and Therapy Systems Division
RISC—Radiology Information System Consortium
RSNA—Radiological Society of North America
SCAR—Society for Computer Applications in Radiology

Published by
SPIE—The International Society for Optical Engineering

Volume 3340

SPIE is an international technical society dedicated to advancing engineering and scientific
applications of optical, photonic, imaging, electronic, and optoelectronic technologies.

The papers appearing in this book comprise the proceedings of the meeting mentioned on the cover and title page. They reflect the authors' opinions and are published as presented and without change, in the interests of timely dissemination. Their inclusion in this publication does not necessarily constitute endorsement by the editors or by SPIE.

Please use the following format to cite material from this book:
   Author(s), "Title of paper," in *Medical Imaging 1998: Image Perception*, Harold L. Kundel, M.D., Editor, Proceedings of SPIE Vol. 3340, page numbers (1998).

ISSN 0277-786X
ISBN 0-8194-2785-3

Published by
SPIE—The International Society for Optical Engineering
P.O. Box 10, Bellingham, Washington 98227-0010 USA
Telephone 360/676-3290 (Pacific Time) • Fax 360/647-1445

Printed in the United States of America.

Contents

SESSION 3   **POSTER SESSION**

Conference Committee

Conference Chair

Harold L. Kundel, M.D., University of Pennsylvania Medical Center

Program Committee

Arthur E. Burgess, Brigham and Women's Hospital/Harvard Medical School
Elizabeth A. Krupinski, Health Sciences Center/University of Arizona
Calvin F. Nodine, University of Pennsylvania Medical Center

Session Chairs

1   Visual Signal Detection
Elizabeth A. Krupinski, Health Sciences Center/University of Arizona

2   Practical Aspects of Perception
Harold L. Kundel, M.D., University of Pennsylvania Medical Center

Keynote Address

From light to optic nerve:
Optimization of the front-end of visual systems

Arthur E. Burgess

Radiology Dept., Brigham and Women's Hospital
Harvard Medical School. 75 Francis St. Boston, MA 02115

ABSTRACT

Blindness in nature is (almost always) fatal. In biology and physiology one finds many situations where nature has obtained neat solutions to problems, solutions that are very nearly the best possible. Many of the design parameters for the eye are not arbitrarily selected, but are constrained to a narrow range of values by physics and information theory considerations. As Helmholtz (1868) mentioned more than a century ago "The eye has every possible defect that can be found in an optical instrument and even some which are peculiar to itself; but they are all so interacted, that the inexactness of the image which results from their presence very little exceeds, under ordinary conditions of illumination, the limits which are set to the delicacy of sensation by the dimensions of the retinal cones." Helmholtz was particularly prescient in his reference to cone dimension because, as we will see, many eye properties are completely determined once cone diameter is selected. The ideas presented in this paper are based on the working assumption that the eye does the best possible job within physical limits. This idea originated with Horace Barlow more than 40 years ago. One excellent reference is the proceedings {*Vision: Coding and Efficiency* (Blakemore, 1990)} of a conference organized to honour Barlow's (nominal) retirement with presentations by his many collaborators over the years. The list includes practically everyone referenced in this paper, which explores the design and optimization of the optics of the eye, retinal transduction and coding of visual data.

OVERVIEW OF PAPER

The design problem can be divided into a number of steps - each with its own optimization considerations. It will be seen that each step leads inexorably to a beautifully optimized system.

a: Select wavelength range, photo-transduction and high gain, low noise pre-amplifier mechanisms.

b: Select retinal matrix material and size of photoreceptors - using waveguide physics.

c: Consider daylight and night operation - resolution by day and sensitivity by night.

d: Select f# (focal length/pupil diameter) - based on photoreceptor size and Nyquist sampling theorem

e: Select simple or compound lens and focal length - depends on body size.

f: Select retinal data encoding method (spatial, temporal, and chromatic) to overcome optic nerve channel capacity limitations, taking into account photon fluctuations, scene statistics and neural noise.

1. LIGHT SPECTRUM CONSIDERATIONS

Summary:

Thermal noise problems at long wavelengths. Problem of UV damage to cells at short wavelengths. 500 nm is the best spectrum peak wavelength at night and 550 nm in the day for terrestrial organisms. There is some biological variation in the peak wavelength for specialized purposes.

Transduction. Sunlight at the surface of the earth covers a spectral range of wavelengths, λ, from 300 nm to more 4000 nm. The human visual system has a narrower tuning, 400 nm to 700 nm, peaked at about 500 nm, as shown in figure 1. Most primates have a similar spectral response. One common misconception is that the sensitivity peak is matched to the solar spectrum peak - not so. The maximum of a continuous emission spectrum has no fixed peak - the peak position depends on the spectral coordinates (wavelength, frequency) and the dependent variable (energy, photon flux) used to plot the graph. In any event, as can be seen in figure 1, the solar spectrum is nearly flat over the human spectral sensitivity range. The basic transducer element in visual systems is a visual pigment consisting of an apoprotein, opsin, covalently linked to 11-cis-retinal (or in rare circumstances 11-cis-dehydroretinal). The retinal molecule undergoes a shape change when a photon is absorbed. This in turn leads to a conductivity change in the membranes of the photoreceptive cells - the result is a very high gain, low-noise multi-stage amplification process (as is good engineering practice). The exact wavelength of the absorption peak is determined by the which one of many opsin molecules is attached to the basic retinal chain. The most fundamental consideration is we live in a world at an absolute temperature of about 300K without refrigerated sensory systems. The activation energy required to initiate the change in shape of the retinal molecule can be delivered either by a photon or by thermal agitation. It would be disastrous to have a high noise level due to thermal activation. Hence, the long wavelength cutoff for visual sensitivity is determined as follows (Vos and van Norren, 1984). Let E (= hc/λ) be the energy needed to active one transducer. The number of spontaneous thermal excitations per second for one rhodopsin molecule with a mean lifetime, $t \approx 10^{-13}$ sec, of a given energy distribution is $q \approx \tau^{-1} \exp(-E/kT)\Sigma[(E/kT)^p/p!]$, where p is the index number for vibrational modes and E is about 70 kT. This gives a single molecule false alarm about once every 10^{10} seconds (≈ 300 years). For the entire monkey rod ($\approx 4\times10^9$ transducer molecules), the observed false alarm rate is about 1 every 180 seconds (Baylor, 1987). Human rods have a similar number. The cone false alarm rate is about one per second. The variation of <u>relative</u> rod false alarm rate that would occur if the sensitivity peak were shifted to longer wavelength is shown by the extremely steep upward line in figure 1. A shift of 200 nm would increase the rate by a factor of 10^7. One lesson from these calculations is how fast the function e^{-ax} changes if 'x' is doubled when 'a' is a large number.

The short wavelength spectral sensitivity cut-off is possibly determined by the risk of molecular damage in the retina from ultraviolet light during daylight hours (Ham et al., 1982). Many animals do have spectral sensitivity well down into the UV region but some also show evidence of retinal damage from extended exposure to high levels of sunlight (Lythgoe,1979). Damage is prevented in primates by a protective pigment in the lens, which increases light absorption dramatically below 400 nm, to ensure that the number of ultraviolet (UV) photons falling on the retina is very low. The curve labeled "relative retinal damage rate" in figure 1 is actually the measured lens pigment absorption factor (from Ham et al.).

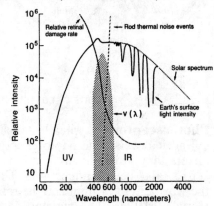

Considering both thermal noise and retina damage constraints, the best compromise choice is a spectral peak around 500 nm. The human night sensitivity curve [scotopic, $V(\lambda)$] is the shaded region in figure 1. Thermal noise is not as important a consideration in daylight because of the much higher photon flux, so a peak at 550 nm is a better choice. Also, the best choice of spectral peak for different species can vary slightly from the above values depending on lifestyle details - fish, for example, live in a variety of spectral environments that are depth dependent. There is still one open question to which no one has been able to answer. Why is the retinal molecule and the transformation from 11-cis to all-trans the basis for photoreception in most, if not all, visual systems?

Fig. 1. Spectral Effects

Amplification. To quote Schnapf and Baylor (1987); "One might naively think that the [photoreceptor] cell would be dormant in the absence of light; in reality, however, the cell is abuzz with activity." There is a difference in ion concentrations across the photoreceptor surface membrane and a flow of sodium and potassium ions. The net loop flow is called the "dark current". When a rod or cone absorbs light, the influx of sodium is blocked for a short time. The dark current is reduced and a negative polarization of the cell interior occurs. The graded potential change (up to -30 mV) propagates to nearby "signal processing" cells. The following summary is based on McNaughton (1990). The isomerized rhodopsin molecule activates up to 500 transductin molecules during random diffusion. Each transductin molecule switches on one phosphodiesterase molecule which in turn breaks down about 500 molecules of 3',5'-cyclic guanosine monophosphate (cGMP). The cGMP molecule interacts cooperatively to open membrane channels that allow passage of about 15 ions during an opening lifetime. The transient reduction in cGMP due to photon absorption blocks some channel opening events. The total gain (about 4×10^6) occurs in three stages and the noise level is intrinsically low. There are 3 dark noise sources. Thermal noise, a low frequency (1/f) noise that is not well understood and also some high frequency noise due to random opening and closing of light-sensitive channels - but both seem to be removed from the signal before it is transmitted to the brain. The variability in response to steady light is little more than that due to photon statistics.

2. EYE OPTICAL DESIGN

Summary:
a: The photoreceptor waveguide should have light confined to its interior -> diameter, p ≈ 2 to 4 λ.
b: Select operation mode: day (angular resolution -> best f#), night (light sensitivity-> low f#).
c: Matching the optics to the retinal grain by optimum (Nyquist) sampling -> best f# in 4 to 8 range.
d: Angular resolution, $\Delta\theta$, needs vary inversely with body height (H) -> focal length, $f = \alpha H$.
e: Simple or compound eye? eye diameter scaling is (d α $\Delta\theta^{-1}$) and (d α $\Delta\theta^{-2}$) respectively.
f: Variety in eye position (front, side) and view angles based on survival needs.
g: Maximize photon transmission through eye media to retina and photon use at retina (e.g. tapitum in cat).

Examples: human and cat eyes. (figure 2) The cornea and lens focus incident light on the retina. Most of the refraction is from the cornea and refractive index gradients in the lens. Lens thickness variation provides adaptive focusing. The (circular) human pupil diameter varies (2 to 8 mm) to control the amount of light entering the eye. The cat has a slit pupil, which allows a much great range of pupil area, and a lens near the middle of the eye to lower the f#. Largest pupil sizes, focal lengths and lowest f# are (human; 8 & 17 mm, f/2) and (cat ; 14 & 12.5 mm, f/0.9). The intraocular media provides mechanical support.

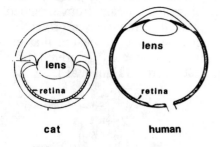

Fig. 2. Cross -sections of cat and human eyes.   Fig. 3. Daylight contrast sensitivity examples.

Photoreceptors - typically consist of a long cylinder with a sequence of plates perpendicular to the cylindrical axis. The photoreceptor boundary acts as a waveguide. The design of this waveguide must ensure that a significant fraction of the light is confined to the interior of the photoreceptor - to avoid "cross-talk" between receptors. The required diameter, p, of this waveguide is completely determined by the wavelength of light and the refractive indices, n_1 and n_2, of the interior and exterior of the waveguide (Snyder, 1975). The waveguide equation, $V=(\pi p/\lambda)[(n_1)^2 - (n_2)^2]^{1/2}$, with 50% confinement at V=2, shows that the minimum feasible diameter for the photoreceptors is on the order of 2 to 4 wavelengths (1 - 2 microns). The uncertainty is due to variation in interior refractive index, n_1 and the difficulty in estimating its value. The 1 to 2 micron photoreceptor minimum diameter holds everywhere in nature, for all species and for both compound and simple eyes.

f-number (f#). The first step is to consider the nature of what is to be imaged. Optical systems can be divided into 2 classes. One, like astronomical telescopes, is designed to image point sources and the sensitivity criteria is the number of photons that fall within the Airy disk diameter. So telescopes have large apertures and focal length is not important as long as the disc is much larger than the grain of the recording medium. The second class is devices, such as cameras, designed to image extended sources (where f# is the quantity to optimize). The visual world consists mainly of extended objects so eyes are members of the second class. For day (high light level) operation the design goal is high resolution - ultimately limited by diffraction. The diameter of the Airy disc is d = 2.44λf#, independent of focal length. The Nyquist theorem gives an optimum of 5 photoreceptors (samples) across the Airy disc, so the best f# choice is f# = 5p/2.44λ =2p/λ = 4 to 7. Birds have a minimum f# of 4. Humans are diffraction-limited for pupil diameter about 2.4 mm (f# = 7). However, it is very difficult to build a diffraction-limited lens using the full lens diameter. Makers of cheap cameras build a large diameter lens and then stop it down with an smaller pupil to obtain good optical quality. Biological optical systems are similar.

Many animals also operate at night. Then vision is limited by photon noise rather than resolution. So photon collection of photons and concentration on the retina should be optimized. Retinal luminance is proportional to $(f^\#)^{-2}$ so it is an advantage to have a low $f^\#$ and optical quality can be sacrificed in order to use the full entrance pupil. Humans have a lowest $f^\#$ of 2; owls, 1.3; cats, 0.9; and some nocturnal insects as low as 0.5. Another desirable feature in low light is efficient use of the photons that enter the eye. For humans; about 2/3 of photons entering the eye reach the retinal surface, about 3/4 of these enter rods, about 1/2 of those are absorbed by rhodopsin molecules, and about 2/3 of absorptions give rise to neural excitation (Barlow, 1981). In many animals the fraction of photon collection at the retina is increased by the presence of a reflective layer (tapetum) directly behind the photoreceptors, which ensures two chances for absorption. The net photon use is about 1/6 for humans and 1/4 for cats (which have a tapetum).

Focal length. As we know from photographs, angular resolution improves when camera focal length increases. The resolution needs of an animal will be determined by survival tasks. Kirschfeld (1976) suggested that the space important to a particular species ought to be measured using its body length as a unit of distance. If this is so - then larger animals would need a better angular resolution to see further and resolution angle would be inversely proportional to body size. Biological variation of angular resolution with body height is illustrated in figure 4 adapted from a marvelous paper by Kirschfeld. Most animals and insects fall within a comparatively narrow band. At the high resolution end one finds birds of prey such as falcons and eagles and predatory mammals. At the low end one encounters a variety of insects. Hence, one concludes that eye focal length ought to be proportional to body size. Note that your cat may be legally blind according to the definition applied to humans (acuity less than 20/200), rats certainly are.

Compound or simple eye? For simple lens eyes, focal length is inversely proportional to resolution angle (fig. 5). For compound eyes, radius is proportional to (res. angle)$^{-2}$ because both the size and number of elements must be increased. Humans would need 30 meter compound eyes to achieve our foveal resolution over the entire eye and 1 meter if resolution varied (Kirschfeld, 1976). Why do insects have compound eyes? It is not feasible to have an image-forming eye less than about 0.5 mm in diameter because photoreceptor length of about 0.2 mm is needed to ensure adequate photon absorption. At 0.5 mm diameter a simple eye would suffer severe aberration off the lens axis, whereas most compound eyes have fixed resolution over the entire visual field. So, it would seem that for small species opt for the latter.

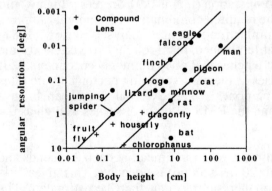

Fig 4. Variation of resolution with body size for example species: both simple and compound eyes. Data is from Kirschfeld (1976) with permission.

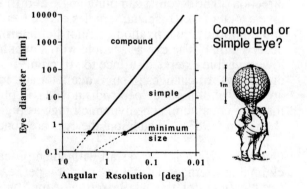

Fig. 5. Variation in the necessary eye size to achieve a desired angular resolution. From Kirschfeld (1976) with permission.

Other species variations. Life in water presents problems for eye design - the following is based on Denny (1993). Terrestrial animals have relatively large refraction at the corneal surface because of the high refractive index difference between air and tissue. That is followed by a variable focus lens which is thin to minimize spherical aberration. In water there is a much smaller corneal refractive index difference, so fish have a smaller radius cornea and a (more refractive) nearly spherical lens with a radially graded refractive index to minimize spherical aberration. Some species have to see both in and out of water; e.g. surface feeding fish, diving mammals, birds and reptiles. A variety of eye designs have evolved to solve these problems. There is also variation due to lifestyle on land; hunters have eyes in the front and limited high acuity angles of view for stereoscopic vision while prey tend to have eyes placed on the sides to obtain a 360 degree view angle. The range of "best" acuity visual angles found in nature is large. "Best" being in a relative sense, since acuity falls off steadily for some maximum value for simple eyes (more on this below). Some animals such as primates have a very rapid decrease from a high central acuity while others (such as rats) start with a lower maximum and have a much shallower gradient. Some birds of prey have an extra design wrinkle - foveal pits shaped like the inside of an ice cream cone. These pits allow cones to be placed at an angle to the incoming light and give an closer cone packing (shorter sampling distance - by a factor of 2) in the direction perpendicular to the light flux. So eagles and hawks have a visual acuity about twice that of humans with eyes of about the same size.

This concludes the discussion of the design of the optics itself. It is interesting to note that the design of the visual system has a number of tight constraints so that parameter selection is far from arbitrary. One presumes that the arrival at nearly optimum values for the design parameters has been mediated by natural selection in which animals with visual systems of suboptimal design would not have as high a survival rate as those with better designs.

3. RETINAL FUNCTION

Summary
a: Aim: convert continuous data to discrete samples in space and time; encode and transmit to cortex
b: Nyquist-sampled input rate at the human retina is 5×10^8 spatial samples over the entire field of view.
c: Temporal sampling need is limited by photon capture rate and depends on light levels.
d: Estimated total data input rate for the entire visual field is about 10^{10} samples/sec. [10^{11} bits/sec.]
e: There are about 10^9 to 10^{10} processing cells and 1.5×10^6 output (ganglion) cells in the retina.
f: The data handling capacity of the cortex is limited so data rates must be reduced at early stages.

Input data rates. The function of the retina is to transduce a continuous 2D luminance pattern and convert it to discrete electrical pulse data for transmission to the brain - where most visual analysis is done in higher animals. The first question to be answered is how finely the sampling and quantization ought to be done. A typical human eye has an angular field of view of about $160°$ (horizontal) by $175°$ (vertical direction). The Nyquist sampling angle at diffraction-limited operation (f/7) is 0.01 degrees which would give a total of 5×10^8 spatial samples over the entire retina. The required combination of temporal sampling and amplitude quantization can not be determined by a similar fundamental analysis. Barlow (1981) observed that "The eye as a whole works over a vast range of luminance, from roughly 10^{-7} cd/m^2 for the lowest visible extended surface to 10^4 cd/m^2 for the brightest patches that one commonly encounters. ... If one allows for changes in pupil diameter and for optical losses ... the corresponding photon capture rates are 10^{-3} photons/sec. per rod and 2×10^5 photons/sec. for cones". The external scene can have a instantaneous luminance dynamic range as high as 1000/1 and the RMS contrast of scenes as high as 0.4 [Laughlin (1983)]. In addition, the eyes are continually moving.

One approach might be to start with an empirical human minimum reaction time of about 0.2 seconds and claim that a temporal sampling rate of 4 per reaction interval (20 per second) is adequate. This gives 10^{10} samples/sec. for the whole retina. Amplitude quantization per sample can then be estimated. The photoreceptor output, v, is proportional to the photon count; $v = an$, with standard deviation, $\sigma_v = (av)^{1/2}$. The appropriate adaptive quantization transformation is square-root $[x(v) = (v/a)^{1/2}]$ which gives σ_x equal to unity. We then must select a quantization step, q, for the transformed data. Let N and N/R be the largest and smallest number of photons per photoreceptor per sampling time interval (50 msec.).The number of steps required is (for large R) equal to $N^{1/2}/q$, independent of R. The best choice of step size is to keep the q/σ ratio between 1 and 0.5 (Burgess, 1985). For $N = 10^4$, the number of required steps is 100 to 200 (7-8 bits). This gives an estimated maximum spatio-temporal data rate of about 10^{11} bits per second.

An alternative approach is to base the combined temporal and amplitude coding on the maximum of 2×10^5 photons/sec., which gives estimate (for a square-root quantization scale) of between 500 and 1000 levels per second. Since there is no particular result to prefer either amplitude or temporal variation over the other, one could use the principle of equipartition of channel capacity and devote half (on a ratio scale) to each - would gives about 30 temporal samples/sec. and 30 amplitude levels per sample. This approach also gives an estimated maximum spatio-temporal data rate of about 10^{11} bits per second.

Overview of the visual system. Cell counts variation in the visual system are shown in figure 6. Unfortunately, the rest of the visual system has a limited processing capability - certainly not enough to handle the full retinal data rate. So some economy of data handling must be introduced at an early stage. The optic nerve has a limited channel capacity and a large fraction (20 to 50%) of the brain is devoted to visual analysis after all the economies introduced by retinal encoding. Retina design features are based on a number of strategies. We do not really need both high spatial and high temporal resolution over the entire visual field. Fast temporal response in the periphery can trigger reflexive eye movement and direct the fovea to the direction of interest. Example visual reaction times are 30 msec. for the fly and 125-200 msec. for man (Land, 1981). At high light levels we can perceive flickering lights up to frequencies of about 80 Hz in the periphery and about 25 Hertz at the fovea. Other problems are to code intensity, colour, and temporal variations. The solution is to use three types of cones (L='Red', M='Green', S='Blue') with antagonistic, circular receptive fields (center/surround, +/- and -/+) and both transient and sustained temporal responses to encode spatio-temporal differences from local means. Analog voltage variations are not suitable for long distance transmission over neural fibers because of rapid attenuation. The physiological solution is to use action potentials - short, two level (on/off) pulses of a fraction of a millisecond in duration and maximum pulse firing rate of about 800 per second - constrained by membrane diffusion time constants. The pulse rate is modulated to represent the amplitude of the peripheral stimulus. The analog to pulse encoding conversion is done by the ganglion cells which act as signal drivers for the optic nerve fibers (which preserve retinal location information for higher level mapping registration). There are many classes of ganglion cells in the retina, 13 in the cat for example (Vaney and Hughes, 1990), but a few types tend to dominate in a particular animal. Individual optic nerve fibers code location in the retina and the number of fibers limits the 2D spatial bandwidth of the system. The ganglion cell firing rate encodes the instantaneous light amplitude at a location and the maximum firing rate limits the range of amplitude coding and temporal bandwidth. There is a lower limit to fiber size because the pulse transmission velocity is inversely proportional to the size, so small fibers would give very sluggish response. There is an upper limit to the number of fibers because of the limited volume of the head. Of course, one might ask why the visual cortex not at the front of the head, instead of the back, to reduce transmission distance.

Retinal cells. A very large number (10^9-10^{10}) of interconnecting cells (hundreds of types) define ganglion cell dendrite (receptive) fields. It should be noted that light must pass through this (transparent) maze of interconnecting fibers and cells before reaching photoreceptors. Even the photoreceptors are 'backwards' - with the transduction region behind the light-insensitive part. This may seem strange from an engineering point of view. Why is this arrangement biologically useful? One possibility is the need for efficient cooling of photoreceptors (Robson, 1998). The image of the sun frequently falls somewhere on the retina and most of this light is absorbed by photoreceptors. Cooling is provided by blood flow and blood vessels are not transparent to light yet must be close to photoreceptors. A good design would be to have blood vessels at the back of the retina and photoreceptors immediately in front of them. The logical place for processing cells is then in front of the photoreceptors.

The following summary of human retinal anatomy is from Wandell (1995). Highest acuity is in the rod and capillary-free foveola (diameter = 0.3 mm, 1°) which has only 50,000 ganglion cells, each with a single cone contributing to the receptive field core and many contributing to the surround. Cone density drops very rapidly in the first 10° relative to the fovea (diameter = 1.5 mm, 5°) to a constant value over the rest of the retina. Cone diameter increases (1.5 ->10 μm) away from the fovea. Outside the fovea there is more than one cone in the central part of a receptive field. Rod density increases rapidly outside the fovea to a maximum at 20° and then decreases slowly. Hundreds of rods contribute to a receptive field. There are two main classes of ganglion cells in the human retina: midget cells (70%) and parasol cells (10%) that seem to transmit complete and independent representations of the visual scene to the cortex. These are referred to as the parvocellular (P) pathway (from midget cells) and the magnocellular (M) pathway (from parasol cells). The two pathways differ significantly in the manner that they encode information. Midget dendritic field sizes increase smoothly from 5 μm in the fovea to 100 μm in the periphery and have a maximum spatial frequency response of 60 cycles/degree. Parasol dendritic field sizes increase from 30 μm near the fovea to 400 μm with best response of 20 cycles/degree. Investigation of the two pathways is still in its early days. The M pathway seems to provide better response to low spatial frequency, high temporal frequency variations (e.g. motion perception). The two pathways also have different contrast-response curves (fig. 9).

4. RETINAL DESIGN

Summary
a: Select acuity variation over the visual field to fit survival needs.
b: Optimize sampling and coding for day or night operation; based on consideration of scene
spatio-temporal statistics and three noise sources (photon, thermal and neural).

Biological Variation in Acuity. Insects and lower animals have smaller data handling problems because of slower resolution needs. Their visual acuity varies little over the visual field. In addition much more analysis and decision capability is built into early stages of their visual systems. Higher level animals tend to have must of their analysis done at cortical levels. One strategy used in such animals to reduce optic nerve transmission and cortical data handling requirements is to vary spatial resolution over the visual field. There are many patterns of acuity inhomogeneity in nature with the selection apparently based on survival tasks (Smythe, 1975). For example (figure 7), birds living in a forest habitat have a single fovea; birds of prey have two fovea connected by a narrow high resolution band; birds that live at sea and in the open plains have broad horizontal fovea that extend across the entire retina. Similar acuity variation is found in mammals. For example, plains animals such as antelopes and cheetahs have highest angular resolution along their visual horizon.

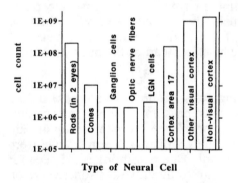

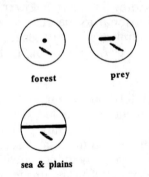

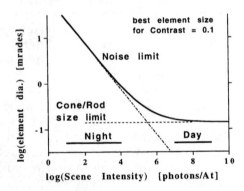

Fig. 6. ß Numbers of different types of cells at various stages (including both eyes).
Data from Wandell (1995)

Fig. 7. Three bird fovea examples The diagonal, feather-like structure is the pecten (highly vascular).

Fig. 8. Variation in optimum size for retinal data acquisition elements with luminance.
Data from Snyder et al.(1977).

Data Acquisition Element Size. At low light levels it is advantageous to connect one ganglion cell to many photoreceptors to create one "data acquisition element". The optimum element size depends of scene intensity and contrast. The following is a summary of Snyder et al. (1977). Their information theory-based analysis was done for a hexagonal lattice of non-overlapping idealized photon acquisition elements that tile the visual field. The quantity to be optimized is the spatial information capacity of the eye [based the maximum number of different pictures that can be constructed for the entire field]. Each element is assumed to be a linear photon counter with a fixed integration time of 0.03 seconds. At high light levels the best element size equals the photoreceptor size. At low light levels, because of photon fluctuations, the optimum strategy is to have large elements that pool the outputs of individual photoreceptors. The best element size also depends of scene contrast. An example plot for 10% contrast is shown in figure 8 with average night and day scene intensities indicated by the horizontal bars. The human cone threshold corresponds to log(relative intensity) of 3 and rod saturation is at 7. The basic message is that an optimum data acquisition system would be adaptive.

Data Encoding #1. (Correlations). Image element intensity values are usually not the most economical transmission coding method - for three reasons. (1) Scene amplitude histograms are very broad and the data dynamic range can be reduced by sending differences. (2) There is usually considerable correlation between neighboring sample values in space and in time and therefore data redundancy. (3) Neural transmission channels are usually degraded by various types of noise, so additional encoding before transmission would ensure that the effects of the anticipated noise are minimized. Different strategies are needed by day and night because of the marked difference in photon flux rate.

By Day. Figure 8 results show that photon fluctuations are not a problem in daylight and so the optimum data acquisition element size is one cone. Human foveal cones have angular diameter of about 0.01° (0.2 milliradians). One popular view is that nerve fibers have a very limited dynamic range and cells are intrinsically noisy. If this view is true, then cells should encode output to minimize the range of values and render fine detail detectable in noise injected by other cells in the processing mosaic. Srinivasan, Laughlin and Dubs (1982) suggest that the retinal strategy is linear predictive coding based on a combination of scene statistics (in both space and time) and neural noise levels. The cell sends the difference between the actual signal found at the central photoreceptor and the local mean intensity. The profile of the receptive field is derived from statistical estimation theory. The definition of 'local' depends on the correlation properties of the scene and the neural SNR. The local region size should increase as the width of the scene autocorrelation function increases. If the neural SNR is high then the local region can be small. If the neural SNR is small then the region ought to be rather large. This strategy has two benefits: (1) It devotes the entire dynamic range to encode a small intensity range and (2) it reduces data redundancy. Srinivasan et al. gave a very nice demonstration that the actual receptive fields used by some insects correspond very well with the very best choice of receptive field design based on these engineering considerations. There is evidence that the fly eye adaptively adjusts its encoding to local visual scene properties (Laughlin, 1990).

By night. As was seen in Figure 8, at night the limiting factor is low photon flux and the resulting input noise. Scene statistics are secondary. So the optimum strategy is to combine rod outputs to increase the size of a "data acquisition" element. Human rod receptive fields cover a range of diameters from 0.1° to 0.8° (2 to 14 milliradians) which nicely matches the element size range suggested in figure 8 for night vision. The final limitation to sensitivity is the intrinsic neural fluctuation noise in the retina. Here again, the cat's level is significantly lower than that of the human. In addition, the cat has a factor of 2.6 advantage in light collection because of a lower f# and a tapetum, so a cat's intrinsic sensitivity to light at night is about 10 times as high as that of a human. One question that has intrigued scientists for a long time is whether we can see single photons at night. The evidence for this will be rather indirect. Data recorded from cat ganglion cells in response to brief flashes of light suggest that they are responsive to single photons. Attempts have been made to determine whether the same is true for humans. The results are still controversial, however there is a suggestion that we in fact need two photon coincidence (within 200 msec) on the retina to provide a perceptual effect.

Data Encoding #2 (Amplitude coding). Once again, there are different optimum strategies for day and night because of the different statistical considerations. The amplitudes that are coded represent differences in luminance (from local mean) normalized by local mean. Again, the principles of data communication tell us that the best transformation is that which gives a uniform probability of firing over the scene dynamic range. During the day, the optimum transformation is based on the cumulative probability distribution of scene contrasts - which is similar to "histogram equalization". This is illustrated in figure 9 with data from the fly (Laughlin, 1983). The dots are measured L-cell response as a function of contrast. The dashed curve is the transfer function of the typical chemical synapse. The solid curve is the cumulative probability of encountering a particular contrast level in a random selection of natural scenes that were obtained using a scanner with similar spectral and angular sensitivity to the fly's eye. Scene measurements suggest that static scene contrast histograms are bi-exponential and spatial contrast variation is scale invariant with a radial spatial frequency power spectrum $S(f) \approx Af^{-2}$ (Ruderman and Bialek, 1994 for example). This hypothesis was also tested by Srinivasan et al. in insect vision and they found a very nice agreement between the theory and biology. A daylight amplitude coding example for a primate is shown in figure 10. The data (from Wandell) are contrast response curves for magnocellular and parvocellular neurons on the lateral geniculate nucleus (LGN) - which acts as a "relay station" between the retina and the visual cortex. The curves through the data are power law functions. At night the main concern is optimum absolute amplitude (rather than contrast) quantization given high photon noise. As was mentioned above, the best strategy is a square-root transformation to allow quantization steps of equal statistical significance. There is evidence for such a result in the cat ganglion cell for small diameter stimuli but the situation is more complex for large stimuli (Barlow and Levick, 1976).

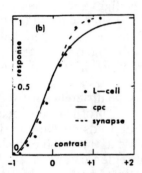

Fig. 9. Response versus contrast for the fly's eye L-cells (dots), synapse transfer function (dashes) and the cumulative probability curve for scenes. From Laughlin (1983) with permission.

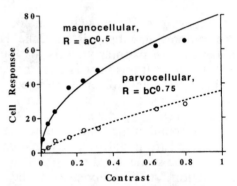

Fig 10. Contrast responses of primate magno-cellular and parvocellar pathways (at LGN). Data of Shapley (1990). From Wandell (p 126) with permission.

Defects. If retinal transduction and coding is done properly, we ought not to be aware of its existence under ordinary circumstances. This is similar to the situation of long distance telephone calls. The telephone handset (imperfectly) converts sound pressure variations into analog electrical signals for short distance transmission. The telephone company uses a variety of encoding strategies for long distance transmission over microwave, fiberoptic, and satellite relay links. If the job is done well we should not be aware of the defects and the limitations imposed by technology.

5. COLOUR

To this point we have been considering transduction and coding of monochromatic light signals. Now we shall turn to the world of colour which involves only cone transduction (not rods). How do cones send colour information to the brain? Historically there have been two theories. The first, known as the trichromatic theory, was proposed by Young in 1800, forgotten, and then revived by Helmholtz in the 1850's. According to this theory there are three visual receptor types that are sensitive respectively to red (R), green (G) and blue (B) light. This is what is found physiologically. The spectral sensitivity curves (fig. 11) are broad and peak wavelengths are: blue (S-cones) at 440 nm, green (M-cones) at 540 nm, and red (L-cones) at 580 nm. This theory agrees with much experimental data. One might ask why we use three colors rather than four or five to represent our colored world? A possible answer is that spectral sensitivity curves are broad relative to range of available wavelengths of light. Applying the Nyquist sampling theorem, Barlow, (1982) showed that three samples completely describe all the colour discriminations that we could possibly make. Some birds have oil droplets at the top of their cones which markedly reduce spectral widths. The birds are able to make use of four or five colour samples and presumably can make superior colour discriminations.

The trichromatic theory had deficiencies and a rival theory (also based on 3 signals) was proposed by Hering in 1878 - now known as the opponent-processing theory. One signal describes luminance variation and the other two are based on four primary colors arranged as opposing pairs using (R-G) and (B-Y) differences. The Hering theory was not met with a high degree of enthusiasm and lay dormant for about 60 years, but through brilliant experimental work it is now recognized that the theory has a great deal to offer. One might then ask which theory is correct. The answer is that both theories appear to be correct. The R, G, and B signals are transformed to the opponent coding scheme at the ganglion cell level for very good information theory reasons. There is a large degree of overlap in the sensitivity curves and therefore redundancy in the output signals. The redundancy in the photoreceptor colour can be removed by a transformation to another coordinate system in which the components are uncorrelated (orthogonal). The B-Y, R-G, and luminance outputs are shown in figure 12. Buchsbaum and Gottschalk (1984) demonstrated that this is, in fact, an optimum (minimum redundancy) coding strategy. Their mathematical predictions agree rather well with the human experimental data.

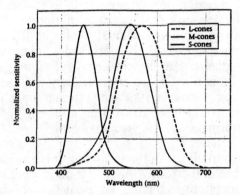

Fig. 11. Absorption spectra for human cones: S (Blue), M (Green), and L (Red). From Wandell, p48 (with permission)

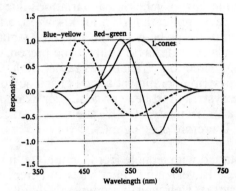

Fig. 12. Spectral responsivity of a set of decorrelated colour sensors under mean daylight conditions. From Wandell, p326 (with permission)

6. THE BRAIN

Visual input data is transmitted to area 17 of the visual cortex. The functions and detailed cellular anatomy of this area has been beautifully mapped by Hubel, Weisel and others over the last 40 years. This work suggests that the visual cortex is constructing a multidimensional feature space that gives highly redundant representations of visual data from both eyes. The human visual cortex, by the way, has an total area of about 1/3 of a credit card. Output from area 17 goes to cortical higher levels. There is also a large amount of feedback - with mapping of higher area cells back to lower area cells. The physiological wiring and the function of these cells and mappings is not yet well understood. However it would appear that at higher levels there is a synthesis of input visual data with a prior knowledge stored in cortical memory and then interpretation of the scene. It is clear from present work that operation on visual data occupies a very significant fraction of the brain. A map of the cortical sheet shows that visual function occupies nearly 50% of the human cortex (Barlow, 1981). There are about 10^{10} neurons in the cortex, 10^{18} synaptic connections and the capability of doing about 10^{16} computations per second! (Watson, 1997)

7. OVERALL EFFICIENCY

Between 1940 and 1960, a number of people set out to determine the absolute performance of the human eye at low light levels. By this, they meant the determination of the fraction of photons entering the eye that were actually used in visual signal detection tasks. They found efficiencies in the order of 5%. In the years following 1950, there were a number of physiological determinations of photon losses in the eye. These measurements suggested an efficiency between the cornea and the optic nerve on the order of 15%. Therefore one might ask what is the source of the disagreement? Actually, they not determining just the efficiency of the components of the eye up to the optic nerve; they were measuring the efficiency of the entire visual system from the cornea to the highest decision centers of the brain. Barlow (1977) measured the efficiency of the central decision making processes using easily visible random dots displayed for a short time on a CRT and found efficiencies in the range from 25% to 50% without any significant suggestion of increased sensitivity to particular spatial patterns.

Since 1980 there have been a number of investigations of statistical decision efficiency for a variety of tasks using noisy gray scale images. The results can be summarized as follows (Burgess, 1990). The efficiencies seem to range from 10 to 75% when display conditions are optimized. The experimental results suggest that humans act as suboptimal Bayesian decision makers - selecting the most likely decision alternative given the available prior information together with the new image data. However we suffer from a variety of shortcomings. These include transduction loses due to the receptive fields and encoding schemes at the retina. This means that humans cannot do detection and discrimination tasks with accuracy limited solely by photon fluctuations. There is a limit to the range in space and time over which we can appreciate correlations (i.e. integrate). Another shortcoming is the existence of internal noise, which can arise from any source of non-reproducible behaviour. This includes physical sources of noise such as neural fluctuations; psychological variations due to variations in attention, motivation; cognitive aspects such as inexact application of prior knowledge to the data collection task (for example imprecise and variable comparisons between the expected signals and the existing signals) and finally - variability in applying decision criteria. In spite of the presence of these limitations, it should be observed that human visual signal detection efficiency is rather high. One need only contemplate the problem of designing a multistage system operating at a total efficiency of 50% to realize that the performance efficiency at each stage in the system must be very good. For example, if one were to construct a 10-stage system to operate at an overall efficiency of 50% then each stage in the system would have to operate at about 93% efficiency. Therefore one ought to be very impressed with the performance of the visual system.

Since we started with a quote from Helmholtz, it seems only fitting to give him the last word. It is evident that he took a Bayesian inference view of perception. The language in the following quotation is archaic, but it is clear that Helmholtz recommends that we think of our perceptions as mental representations of the object most likely to explain the sensory input [Wandell, p282]. The Helmholtz quote is: "The general rule determining the ideas of vision that are formed whenever an impression is made on the eye, is that *such objects are always imagined as being present in the field of vision as would have to be there in order to produce the same impression on the nervous mechanism.*" [Italics in the original]

This brief presentation about visual systems is just one part of the marvelous story of the whys and wherefores of comparative physiology. For those who want to pursue the topic much further I can highly recommend books by Denny, Wandell and Withers - there, of course, many others that can be read with delight. One last personal note is that if I had my life to live over, given what I now know, certainly one decision would have been different - I would have become a physiologist.

8. ACKNOWLEDGMENTS

I would like to thank Simon Laughlin and John Robson (physiologists) for their many constructive suggestions on a draft of this manuscript and their patience with the gross oversimplifications of a mere physicist. John had a particularly nice observation - he called the approach used in this paper "inverse optimization". Given an optimum solution - determine the problem and the constraints.

9. REFERENCES

DL Ruderman and W Bialek. Statistics of Natural Images: Scaling in the woods.
    Phys. Rev. Letters. 73, 814-817 (1994)
HB Barlow. The Efficiency of Detecting Changes in Density of Random Dot Patterns.
    Vision Res. 18, 637-650 (1978)
 HB Barlow. Critical Limiting Factors in the Design of the Eye and Visual Cortex. Ferrier Lecture.
        Proc.Roy.Soc.B212, 1-34 (1981)
HB Barlow. What causes trichromaticity? A theoretical analysis using comb-filtered spectra.
    Vision Res. 22, 635-43 (1982)
DA Baylor. Photoreceptor Signals and Vision - Proctor Lecture.

Invest. Opthal. and Visual Sci. 28, 34-49 (1987).

AE Burgess, Effect of Quantization Noise on Visual Signal Detection in Noisy Images.
J. Opt. Soc. Am. A2, 1424-1428 (1985).

AE Burgess, High Level Visual Decision Efficiencies. in Vision: Coding and Efficiency,
C. Blakemore (edit.), Cambridge Univ. Press (1990)

G.Buchsbaum and A.Gottschalk. Trichromacy, Opponent Colour Coding and Optimum Colour
Information Transmission in the Retina. Proc.Roy.Soc. (London) B220, 89-113 (1983)

HJA Dartnell. The interpretation of Spectral Sensitivity Curves. Brit. Med. Bull. 9, 24-30 (1953)

MW Denny. Air and Water: The Biology and Physics of Life's Media.
Princeton Univ. Press, Princeton NJ (1993)

WT Ham, HA Mueller, JJ Ruffolo, D Guerry III, and RK Guerry. Action Spectrum for Retinal Injury
from Near-ultraviolet Radiation in the Aphakic Monkey. Am. J. Opthal. 93, 299-306 (1982).

H. von Helmholtz.The Recent Progress of the Theory of Vision. (1868)
Republished in: Popular Lectures by Hermann von Helmholtz. Dover, NY (1962)

K Kirschfeld. The Resolution of Lens and Compound Eyes. In: Neural Principles in Vision.
Edit.R.Weiler, Springer, Berlin (1976)

MF Land. Optics and Vision in Invertebrates. In: Handbook of Sensory Physiology,
Vol.VII/6B. Edit.H.Autrum. Springer-Verlag, Berlin (1981)

SB Laughlin, Matching Coding to Scenes to Enhance Efficiency. In Physical and Biological Processing
of Images, OJ Braddick and AC Sleigh (edit.), Springer-Verlag Berlin (1983)

SB Laughlin, Coding Efficiency and Visual Processing. In Vision: Coding and Efficiency,
C. Blakemore (edit.), Cambridge Univ. Press (1990)

JN Lythgoe; Ecology of Vision, Clarendon Press, Oxford (1979)

PA McNaughton. The light response of photoreceptors. In Vision: Coding and Efficiency,
C. Blakemore (edit.), Cambridge Univ. Press (1990)

J Robson, personal communication (1998)

JL Schnapf and DA Baylor. How Photoreceptor Cells Respond to Light.
Scientific American 256, 40-47 (April, 1987)

R. Shapley. Visual sensitivity and parallel retinocortical channels. Ann. Rev. Psy. 41,635-658((1990)

RH Smythe. Vision in the Animal World. St. Martin's Press (1975)

AW Snyder, Photoreceptor optics - theoretical principles. In: Photoreceptor Optics.
AW Snyder and R Menzel (edits) Springer. NY (1975)

AW Snyder, SB Laughlin and DG Stavenga. Information Capacity of Eyes.
Vision Res. 17, 1163-1175(1977)

AW Snyder, TJ Boosmaier and A Hughes. The Theory of Comparative Eye Design.
In Vision: Coding and Efficiency, C. Blakemore (edit.), Cambridge Univ. Press (1990)

MV Srinivasan, SB Laughlin and A Dubs. Predictive Coding: A Fresh View of Inhibition in the Retina.
Proc.Roy.Soc.B216, 427-459 (1982)

A.J.Van Doorn, W.A.Van de Grind and J.J.Koenderink, (Editors). Limits in Perception,
VNU Science Press, Utrecht (1984)

BA Wandell. Foundations of Vision. Sinauer Associates Ltd. Sunderland, MA (1995)

A Watson. Why can't a computer be more like a brain. Science 277, 1934-1936 (1997)

PC Withers. Comparative Animal Physiology. Saunders College Pub., NY (1992)

SESSION 1

Visual Signal Detection

Human vs. model observers in anatomic backgrounds

Miguel P. Eckstein[a], Craig K. Abbey[b], James S. Whiting[a]

[a]Department of Medical Physics & Imaging
Cedars Sinai Medical Center
Los Angeles, CA 90048-1865

[b]Department of Radiology
Arizona Health Sciences Center
University of Arizona

ABSTRACT

Model observers have been compared to human performance detecting low contrast signals in a variety of computer generated backgrounds including white noise, correlated noise, lumpy backgrounds, and two component noise. The purpose of the present paper is to extend this work by comparing a number of previously proposed model observers (non-prewhitening matched filter, non-prewhitening matched fitler model with an eye filter, Hotelling observer and channelized-Gabor Hotelling observer model) to human visual detection performance in real anatomic backgrounds (x-ray coronary angiograms). Human and model observer performance are compared as a function of increasing added white noise. Our results show that three of the four models (the non-prewhitening matched filter, the Hotelling and channelized-Gabor Hotelling) are good predictors of human performance.

Keywords: Medical image perception, visual signal detection, model observers, structured backgrounds, anatomic backgrounds, filter models.

1.INTRODUCTION

Medical image quality can be objectively measured in terms of human performance in tasks that are relevant to visual clinical diagnosis.[1] In this context, one method to assess medical image quality is to conduct a psychophysical study (Receiver Operating Characteristic, ROC study). However, ROC studies are not feasible for optimization problems where the number of parameters to investigate is large. For this reason, investigators have tried to develop computer observer models that can accurately predict human performance as a function of basic image properties such as image processing and acquisition techniques. This model could be potentially used for fast-automated evaluation and optimization of medical image quality. [1]

Previous investigators have compared model observer performance and human performance in computer generated noise. A large number of studies have investigated human vs. model performance in white noise that approximates medical image noise of quantum origin.[2-5] Subsequently, investigators have investigated performance in more complex backgrounds such as filtered white noise,[6] backgrounds with random inhomogeneities[7,8] (lumpy backgrounds), and combinations of white and low-pass filtered noise[9] ("2-component noise").

Fewer studies have compared human and model performance in real anatomic backgrounds[*].[10,11] The reason being these latter studies present several difficulties including gathering of a large amount of clinical images, developing a technique to generate realistic computer simulated signals to be embedded in the real backgrounds, and estimating model observer performance from samples rather than from mathematically closed form expressions. [13]

---

[*] Anatomic backgrounds are also referred to as structured backgrounds, a term first coined by Revesz and Kundel. [10]

The present paper extends the application of model observers to real medical image backgrounds. We compare human and model observer performance in anatomic backgrounds as a function of increasing added white noise. The goal of the present paper is to assess whether we can obtain an observer model that can predict the effect of adding increasing amounts of white noise to the anatomic background. A secondary goal of this paper is to determine whether the output correlation of the models are approximately Gaussian distributed and therefore whether d' (to be defined later) can be used as a figure of merit for model observer performance in real anatomic backgrounds.

2. THEORY

2.1.Model observers

Nearly all of the model observers currently used in medical imaging are linear models. The model observers compare a template with the data by computing the correlation at each of the possible signal locations. The observer then makes a decision based on the output correlation. For an alternative forced choice (AFC) task where the signal appears in one of M locations, the model observer is assumed to obtain the template output at each location and select the location that elicited the highest response. The general form for all models is as follows:

$$\lambda = \sum_{x=1}^{N} \sum_{y=1}^{N} w(x,y) l(x,y) \tag{1}$$

where λ is the correlation output, $w(x,y)$ is the 2-dimensional template, $l(x,y)$ is the data at a given locations.

A convenient and often used framework for model observer is the use of a matrix formulation. [1,6,13] We can adopt the matrix formulation by ordering the elements of the N x N template into N^2 x 1 column vector and doing the same with the data. In the matrix formulation the correlation is given by: [1,13]

$$\lambda = \sum_{n=1}^{N^2} w_n l_n = w^t l \tag{2}$$

where w^t and l are vectors and the superscript t refers to the transpose.

The variety of current model observers differs mainly in two aspects. First, models differ in the prior knowledge they use to derive the template. For example, some models use information about the signal and others use information about the signal and the background statistics. Second, given that these models are attempting to predict human performance many of them include information-processing constraints in the human visual system based on previous psychophysical or physiological findings. Therefore models differ in the components they include to reflect constraints imposed by human visual system. For example, some models might include the differential sensitivity of the human visual system to different spatial frequencies, or internal neural noise, or processing by a set of spatial frequency tuned channels, etc. Although there are large number of variations of models that might be tested, in the present paper we focus on four models: non-prewhitening matched filter, non-prewhitening matched filter with an eye filter, Hotelling observer and channelized Hotelling. The following is a brief description of the templates used by each of these models.

2.1.1. Non-Prewhitening Matched Filter (NPWMF)

The NPWMF has a long history of application in medical imaging[1,2,3,14] and consists of a template that exactly matches the signal profile: $w(x,y) = s(x,y)$. This approach is optimal in white noise but becomes suboptimal in correlated noise because the model has inability to prewhiten the noise ("undo the correlations").

2.1.2. Non-Prewhitening Matched Filter with Eye filter (NPWE)

The non-prewhitening matched filter eye filter (NPWE; also known as the modified non-prewhitening matched filter) also uses information about the signal but takes into account the differential human visual sensitivity to different spatial frequencies. This model has been previously used by Ishida[15] and Burgess[16] among others. The effective template used by the observer is given by:

$$w(x,y)= FFT^{-1}[s(u,v) |E(u,v)|^2]$$ (3)

where FFT is the inverse fast-fourier transform, s(u,v) is the signal amplitude in the frequency domain and E(u,v) is the contrast sensitivity function and is given by:

$$E(f)= f^{1.3} c \exp(-f^2)$$ (4)

where $f = sqrt(u^2 +v^2)$ is the spatial frequency in the radial direction in cycles per degree. The value of c is set so that the contrast sensitivity function peaks at about 4.0 cycles/degree. The contrast sensitivity is identical to that used by Burgess. [16]

2.1.3. Hotelling observer (with square spatial windowing):

The Hotelling observer is the best linear observer when statistics are approximately Gaussian. [1,7] The Hotelling observer derives a template that takes into account knowledge about not only the signal profile but also the background statistics. In white noise the Hotelling observer becomes the matched filter. However, in correlated noise, the Hotelling observer derives a template that decorrelates the noise prior to matched filtering. The template for the Hotelling observer can be derived from the variance covariance matrix of the background: [1,6,13]

$$w_h= K^{-1} [<s+b>-<b>]$$ (5)

where w_h is a $1 \times N^2$ matrix with the elements of the template, K^{-1}, the inverse of the variance covariance matrix, is a $N^2 \times N^2$ matrix, <s+b> is the mean signal plus background vector, and <b> is the mean background vector.

2.1.4. Channelized Hotelling (Gabor channels):

The channelized Hotelling observer is similar to the Hotelling but is constrained by a reduction in information content by the processing through the channels. The channelized Hotelling template is the best template that can be derived from a linear combination of the channels.   There are number of different channelized Hotelling models in the literature including square channels,[17,18] difference of Gaussians,[9,19] difference of Mesa filters[9] and Gabor channels. [11,12]   In this paper we use a Gabor channel mechanism. Marcelja[20] used Gabor mathematical functions to model the response of cells in area V1 of the cat. Watson[21] subsequently used these functions for his model of spatial form. The Gabor channels are given by: [21]

$$V(x, y) = \exp\left[- 4(\ln 2) \frac{(x^2 + y^2)}{w_s^2} \right] \cos[2\pi f(x \cos \theta + y \sin \theta) + \beta]$$ (6)

where f is the spatial frequency, θ is the orientation, W_s is the width and β is the phase. The Fourier transform of a Gabor channel is a Gaussian function centered at the center frequency f and with a half-height full width given by $W_f =0.8825 W_s$. Another way of measuring the width in the frequency domain of the Gabor channel is in octave bandwidth defined as:

$$bandwidth = \log 2 \left[\frac{f + (W_f / 2)}{f - (W_f / 2)} \right]$$ (7)

where f is the central frequency and W_f is as previously defined.

In this particular paper we used 5 a channel model with 5 spatial frequencies (central frequencies, 32, 16, 8, 4 and 2 cycles per degree), 5 orientations ($0°$, $72°$, $144°$, $210°$ and $284°$), and two phases (odd and even) resulting in a total of 50 channels. The spatial frequency bandwidth of the channels was approximately 0.9 octaves.

The Hotelling decision rule can be used to determine the best linear combination of the output of the channels to maximally discriminate between signal location and non-signal location. These weights are given by: [13,18,22]

$$\alpha = K_V^{-1} \left[<s_V+b_V> - <b_V> \right] \tag{8}$$

where α is a matrix containing the optimal weights for each of the Gabor channels, K_V is a N x N matrix describing the variance covariance matrix of the output of the channels to the images. For our particular implementation the variance covariance matrix consisted of a 50 x 50 matrix. Finally $<s_V+b_V>$ is a vector containing the mean signal plus background as seen by each channel and $<b_V>$ is the mean background as seen by each channel. The best template that can be constructed from the channels can be estimated from the obtained weights by performing a linear combination of the channels:

$$w_V(x, y) = \sum_{i=0}^{N} \alpha_i \cdot V_i(x, y) \tag{9}$$

2.2. Template estimation from samples (Hotelling vs Fisher discriminant)

Calculation of the templates for the Hotelling models requires information about the statistical properties of the background contained in the variance/covariance matrix. Unlike previous work where the variance/covariance matrix is known in advance because the noise is computer generated, in the present work the variance/covariance matrix has to be estimated from samples. This brings us to a distinction pointed out by Barrett et al.[22] The Hotelling discriminant (or template) is a population parameter estimated from the ensemble variance/covariance matrix. However, when the population variance covariance matrix is unknown then one is estimating a population template from samples. The estimated template is composed of random variables which variability depends on the number of samples used in the estimation and the degrees of freedom of the template. The template estimated from the samples referred to as the Fisher-discriminant. In order to obtain the Fisher-discriminant (template from samples) one needs to estimate the variance covariance from the samples. However, estimating a covariance matrix for a 512 x 512 image becomes computationally intractable due to the large number of samples needed. In this paper, the dimensionality of the variance covariance matrix is reduced by taking windows of 12 x 12 pixels centered at the possible signal locations. The calculation of the resulting 144 x144 variance-covariance matrix was based on 2000 independent samples (which were different from the testing image set used in the human performance study and for obtaining model observer performance). Estimating the Hotelling template through this windowing method restricts the Fisher-discriminant spatially and might result in systematic differences between the sample derived template and the population template. An alternative method to more efficiently estimate a template from samples using Laguerre-Gauss functions is discussed in detail by Barrett, et al[22] in this same volume.

2.3 Figures of merit

An important issue is how to quantify model observer performance in anatomic backgrounds. One basic way that makes no assumptions about the output correlation statistics is to compute the probability of the ouput to the signal location taking a larger value than the maximum output to the background only locations, Prob($\lambda_{s,b} > \max(\lambda_b)$).One can estimate this probability from samples by tallying the percent of trials where the model correctly identifies the signal location. This can be mathematically expressed as: [13]

$$\hat{P}c = \frac{1}{J} \sum_{j=0}^{J} step(\lambda_{s,b} - \max(\lambda_{bi})) \tag{10}$$

where $\lambda_{s,bi}$ is the output correlation to the signal plus background at location i in trial j, $\lambda_{s,b}$ is the output correlation to background only location, J is the total number of trials, step is one when the argument is larger than zero and is zero when the argument is less than zero. The function max takes the maximum among the output correlations to the M-1 non-signal locations. Equation 10 simply tallies the number of trials in which the model observer correctly located the signal.

When the output correlation of the model observer's template is Gaussian distributed for the signal plus background location and background only locations, then a convenient figure of merit is d', index of detectability defined as:

$$d' = \frac{<\lambda_{s,b}> - <\lambda_b>}{\sqrt{\frac{1}{2}(\sigma^2_{s,b} + \sigma^2_b)}} \tag{11}$$

where $<\lambda_{s,b}>$ is the mean template output to the signal plus background, $<\lambda_b>$ is the mean template output to the background only and $\sigma_{s,b}$ and σ_b are the standard deviation of the template to the signal plus bakckground and background only locations respectively.

When the output correlation of the models is Gaussian distributed then d' can be related to Pc by the following expression:

$$Pc(d',M) = \int_{-\infty}^{+\infty} g(x - d'_g)[G(x)]^{M-1} dx \tag{12}$$

where

$$g(x) = \frac{1}{\sqrt{2\pi}} \exp[-x^2 / 2]$$

G(x) is the cumulative Gaussian and M is the number of alternatives in the experiment

3.METHODS

Human psychophysical studies: The test images consisted of a computer simulated signal and real medical backgrounds extracted from x-ray coronary angiograms. The signal was a hemi-ellipsoidal filling defect (clinically known as thrombus) embedded within one of four computer simulated arterial segments (4 AFC). The signal appeared as a brighter blurred disk. The observer's task from trial to trial was to correctly identify the signal locations. Observers participated in 5 experimental conditions consisting of increasing levels of added white noise: root mean square (RMS) values of 0, 0.071, 0.125, 0.18, and 0.25. For each white noise level there were 5 different signal contrast conditions. Details about the testimage generation algorithm and the experimental methods can be found in Eckstein et al.[23,24]

The data reported in the present paper corresponds to human performance for a signal with square root signal contrast energy of 0.405. The human performance detecting a signal with that contrast was inferred from a psychometric function that was fit to the d' vs signal contrast data for each level of added white noise. For the purposes of the present paper the psychometric function was a linear function between d' and signal contrast with a 0 x-intercept, therefore assuming no sources of uncertainty[25]. [†]
The d' vs. signal contrast data did show a small degree of uncertainty[23] for high levels of added white noise but was ignored in this paper. Therefore the human performance predictions reported in this paper for the two highest white noise levels overestimate by a small amount actual human performance. The rationale to exclude sources of uncertainty in the predicted human performance for a given signal contrast was that the model observers presently do not contain sources of uncertainty. Therefore, it might be an unfair

---

[†] In Eckstein, Ahumada, and Watson[23] the data are fit with psychometric functions that allow for sources of uncertainty.

comparison to compare them with human data that presents sources of uncertainty. We plan to include these sources of uncertainty in the model observers in the near future.

4. RESULTS AND DISCUSSION

4.1. Figures of merit for model observers

We first report performance for the model observers in the condition with no added white noise as quantified in two different ways. Pc was tallied using Equation 10 for model performance in the 100 images viewed by the human observers.[‡] Then it was transformed to d'_g using the Gaussian assumption from Equation 12. Secondly, we computed d' directly from the template outputs by computing the distance in standard deviation units between the distribution for the models' output to the signal plus background and background only (Equation 11). If the output correlation of the model templates are approximately Gaussian distributed then these two figures of merit (d' and d'_g) should not be significantly different. Table 1 summarizes performance as measured by the two figures of merit for each of the models for the condition with only anatomic background and no added white noise. Standard errors for the estimated model predictions were calculated by propagating the binomial error to d' by method of partial derivatives.[24,26] For all models the two metrics d'_g and d' did not differ significantly (p > 0.05).

Figure of merit	NPWMF	NPWE	Hotelling	Channel-Hotelling
d'_g (from P_c)	0.715 ± 0.15	3.45 ± 0.38	3.45 ± 0.38	2.84 ± 0.25
d'	0.4 ± 0.15	3.00 ± 0.27	3.31 ± 0.32	2.95 ± 0.27

TABLE 1

Based on these (and looking at the histograms of the output correlation), we can conclude the models' output correlation are approximately Gaussian distributed and the use of d' as defined by Equation 11 is a reasonable figure of merit to quantify model observer performance in real x-ray coronary angiogram backgrounds. In addition, d' can be related to Pc in an alternative forced choice through Equation 12. Future research should test the assumption in a more stringent manner by using a larger number of sample test-images.

4.2. Absolute performance of the models

Figure 1 shows d' (computed from Pc using Equation 12) for all models and human observers as a function of increasing added white noise (RMS noise). Performance for the NPWMF is lower than human performance for all conditions. We had previously reported this result and related the NPWMF poor performance to the model's inability to compute contrast rather than absolute luminance. In this way, any increases in the local luminance (dc) of a non-signal location will deceive the NPWMF model to elicit a higher response. Others have reported similar deficit for the performance of NPWMF in lumpy backgrounds.[7,16]

Performance for the NPWE, Hotelling observer and Channelized Hotelling observer are approximately about a factor of 2 better than human performance in the condition with no added white noise (only anatomic background). A rather interesting result is that we found a small difference for the performance of the Hotelling observer model and the NPWE model for the condition containing only anatomic background. Burgess et al have found that the NPWE and Hotelling model perform at similar levels in absolute performance in 2-component noise with Gaussian-low pass noise with correlation distances (standard deviation of Gaussian blurring function) of 0.1 to approximately 2 pixels.[9]

Interestingly as the white noise is increased, Figure 2 shows that the NPWE becomes increasingly suboptimal compared with the Hotelling model. This is because as the white noise is increased, the Hotelling observer adapts by increasing the weights of lower frequency components of the images. These low-frequency components are strongly attenuated by the eye filter and hence not optimally used by the

---

[‡]Given that model observer performance is based on a limited number of sample images, reported performance levels might differ from model observer performance in the ensemble set of images (infinite number of images).

NPWE observer. The channelized (Gabor) Hotelling model lies for most part in between the Hotelling and the NPWE model; however it performs more poorly than the NPWE for the condition with no added white noise. Results of the channelized Hotelling model are sensitive to the particular number, center spatial frequency and bandwidth of the channels. We did not systematically investigate these parameters for the current paper.

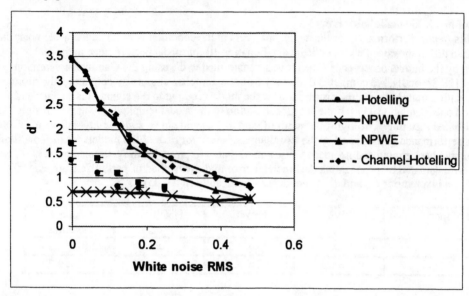

Figure 1. Absolute performance as measured by d' for model observers and two human observers (data points with no connecting line).

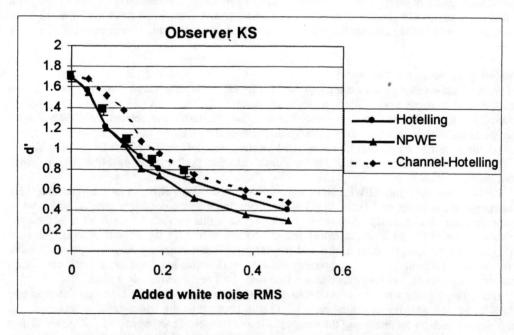

Figure 2. Model observer performance as measured by d' scaled to match human performance (KS, data points with no connecting line) in the condition with no added white noise.

4.3. Predicting the effect of increasing white noise

There are two common ways in which model performance is compared to human performance. The first one is by scaling model observer performance to match human performance at one of the conditions. A second is to include sources of degradation that are known to be present in the human observer such as sources of internal noise.

We first compare model observer and human performance by scaling the predictions for each model observer so as to match human performance in the anatomic background condition with no added white noise. Figure 2 and 3 show the result of scaling the different models in this way. The graphs show that all three models give a quantitative good fit to the human data. Goodness of fit measures were not computed to verify whether one model gave a significantly better fit. Our results show that our experimental paradigm is perhaps not the best to differentiate across models. On the other hand our experimental choice is based on clinical relevance and therefore it argues that for the task at hand (effect of white noise on detection on x-ray coronary angiograms) using any of these three models will generate reasonable predictions.

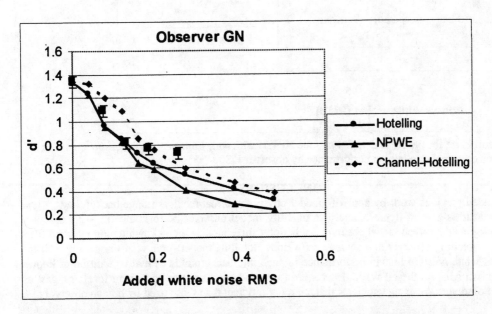

Figure 3. Model observer performance as measured by d' scaled to match human performance (GN, data points with no connecting line) in the condition with no added white noise.

We are also currently attempting to reduce model observer performance to human levels by including additional sources of degradation such as internal noise. In this paper we report performance for the NPWE with the addition of a number of internal noise components. These internal noise components were estimated from psychophysical experiments[23] that attempted to measure the amount of white noise that has to be added to the image to degrade human performance by an equivalent amount as the degradation produced by different internal noise components. These experiments estimated a constant internal noise (for our display conditions) with an rms = 0.032 and an internal noise component induced by the presence of the anatomic background with an rms = 0.049. In addition, we include a second induced internal noise component due to the presence of the white noise in the image equal to 0.6 the rms of the external white noise estimated by experiments by Burgess and Colborne. [4] These three known internal noise components were added to the NPWE model in order to reduce its performance to human levels.[§] The addition of the internal noise was implemented by adding variability to the output of the NPWE model.

Figure 4 shows the NPWE without and with the internal noise components and human performance for our observer with the highest performance (KS). The results show that even when we include known and measured sources of degradation to the NPWE, the model still outperforms the human by a large margin. These results might suggest that our models use templates that are more efficient than those used by human performance.

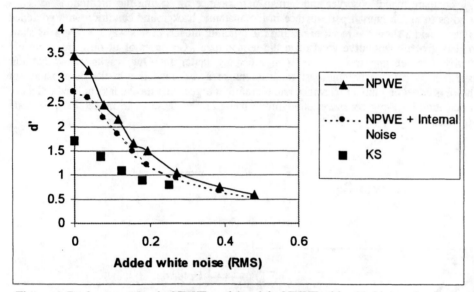

Figure 4. Performance for the NPWE model and the NPWE with added internal noise components. Square symbols correspond to human performance by observer KS.

5. CONCLUSIONS

We have extended previous work by applying model observers to real medical image backgrounds. Our results show that d' is a valid figure of merit to quantify model observer performance in x-ray coronary angiogram backgrounds. When model observer predictions, three models (non-prewhitening matched filter with eye filter, Hotelling observer and channelized-Gabor Hotelling model) predicted reasonably well the effect of added white noise to human performance in anatomic backgrounds. Finally, addition of known sources of internal noise to the NPWE did not seem to degrade performance to human levels suggesting that our model observers are using templates that are more efficient than those used by human observers.

6. ACKNOWLEDGEMENTS

This was work was supported by National Institute of Health (NIH) grants RO1 HL53455 and RO1 CA5643.

7. REFERENCES

1. Barrett HH, Yao J, Rolland JP, Myers KJ. Model observers for assessment of image quality. Proc. Natl.Acad. Sci. USA, 90:9758- 9765, 1993.

2. Burgess AE, Wagner RB, Jennings RJ, and Barlow HB. Efficiency of human visual signal discrimination. Science, 214: 93-94, 1981

[§] The experimental paradigm to estimate equivalent internal noise assumes that the observer uses a fixed filter for all white noise conditions. Therefore we did not attempt to include these internal noise estimates in models that violate this assumption as with adaptive filter models (e.g. Hotelling models).

3. Burgess AE, Ghandeharian H. Visual signal detection. II. Signal location identification. J. Opt. Soc. Am. A, 1: 900-905 , 1984

4. Burgess AE, Colborne B. Visual Signal Detection IV: Observer inconsistency. J. Opt. Soc. Am. A, 5:617-627, 1988.

5. Swesson RG, Judy, PF, Detection of noisy visual targets: model for the effects of spatial uncertainty and signal to noise ratio. Percept. Psychophys, 29: 521-534, 1981

6. Myers KJ, Barrett HH, Borgstrom MC, Patton, DD, Seeley GW. Effect of noise correlation on detectability of disk signals in medical imaging. J. Opt. Soc. Am.A , 2: 1752-1759, 1985

7. Rolland JP, Barrett HH. Effect of random inhomogeneity on observer detection performance. J. Opt. Soc. Am. A, 9:649-658, 1992.

8. Abbey, CK, Barrett HH, Linear iteriative reconstruction algorithms: Study of observer performance, in Proc. 14th Int. Conf. On Information Processing in Medical Imaging (Yves Bizais, Christian Barillot, and Robert Di Paola, Eds.), Kluwer Academic, Dordrecht, 65-76, 1995

9. Burgess AE, Li X., Abbey C.K., Visual signal detectability with two noise components: anomalous masking effects, J. Opt. Soc. Am. A 14(9):2420-2442, 1997.

10 . Revesz G, Kundel HL, Graber MA. The influence of structured noise on the detection of radiologic abnormalities. Invest. Radiol., 9:479-486, 1974

11. Eckstein MP, Whiting JS. Lesion detection in structured noise. Academic Radiology, 2:249-253, 1995

12. Eckstein, MP, Whiting JS, Using computer observer models to predict the effect of JPEG image compression on human lesion detection, Optics & Photonics News, Vol. 5 No 8, Opt. Soc Am. (Suppl), 128, 1994.

13. Abbey CK, Barrett HH, Eckstein MP. Practical issues and methodology in assessment of image quality using model observers. in Medical Imaging Proc. SPIE, Ed. H Roerhig The physics of medical imaging, 3032: 182-194, 1997.

14. Wagner RF, Weaver KE. An assortment of image quality indices for radiographic film-screen combinations- can they be resolved? In Application of Optical Instrumentation in Medicine I. P.L. Carson, W. H. Hendee, and W.C. Zarnstorff, eds, Proc. SPIE, 35, 83-94. 1972.

15. Ishida M., Doi K., Loo LN, Metz CE, Lehr JL, Digital image processing: effect of detectability of simulated low-contrast radiographic patterns, " Radiology 150, 569-575, 1984.

16. Burgess AE. Statistically defined backgrounds: Performance of a modified nonprewhitening matched filter model. J. Opt. Soc. Am. A, 11:1237-42, 1994

17. Myers K., Barrett HH, Addition of a channel mechanism to the ideal observer model, J Opt. Soc. Am. A, 4: 2447-2457, 1987.

18. Yao J, Barrett HH, Predicting human performance by a channelized hotelling observer model, SPIE Math. Methods Med. Imaging, 1768:161-168, 1992

19. Abbey CK, Barrett HH, Wilson DW, Observer signal to noise ratios for the ML-EM algorithm, Proc. SPIE 2712:47-58, 1996.

20. Marcelja S., J. Opt. Soc. Am. A, 70, 1297-1300. 1980

21. Watson AB, Detection and recognition of simple spatial forms, in Physical and Biological Processing of Images, O.J. Bradick & A.C. Sleigh, Eds. New York: Springer-Verlag. 1983

22. Barrett HH, Abbey CK, Gallas and B, Eckstein MP, Stabilized estimates of Hotelling-observer detection performance in patient structured noise, Proc. SPIE 3340, 1998

23. Eckstein MP, Ahumada AJ Jr, and Watson AB, Visual signal detection in structured backgrounds II. Effects of contrast gain control, background variations, and white noise, J. Opt. Soc. Am. A. 14:2406-2419, 1997

24. Ecksein MP, Whiting JS, Visual signal detection in structured backgrounds I. Effect of number of possible locations and signal contrast, J Opt. Soc. Am. A, 13:1777-1787, 1996.

25. Pelli DG, Uncertainty explains many aspects of visual contrast detection and discrimination, J. Opt. Soc. Am. A., 2:1508-1530, 1985

26. Burgess AE, Comparison of receiver operating characteristic and forced choice observer performance measurement methods, Med. Phys., 22(5): 643-655, 1995

STABILIZED ESTIMATES OF HOTELLING-OBSERVER DETECTION PERFORMANCE IN PATIENT-STRUCTURED NOISE

Harrison H. Barrett[*†], Craig K. Abbey[†] and Brandon Gallas[†]
Department of Radiology
Arizona Health Sciences Center
University of Arizona
Tucson, AZ 85724

Miguel Eckstein
University of California at Los Angeles
Cedars Sinai Medical Center
Los Angeles, CA

ABSTRACT

This paper addresses the question of how to determine the performance of the optimum linear or Hotelling observer when only sample images are available. This observer is specified by a template from which a scalar test statistic is computed for each image. It is argued that estimation of the Hotelling template is analogous to problems in image reconstruction, where many difficulties can be avoided through judicious use of prior information. In the present problem, prior information is enforced by choice of the representation used for the template. We consider specifically a representation based on Laguerre-Gauss functions, and we discuss ways of estimating the coefficients in this expansion from sample images for the problem of detection of a known signal. The method is illustrated by two experiments, one based on simulated nonuniform fields called lumpy backgrounds, the other on real coronary angiograms.

1. INTRODUCTION

It is often useful to express the results of human perceptual studies in the form of an efficiency, defined as the ratio of the human performance to that of some standard or ideal observer. For signal-detection or classification tasks, performance of both the human and the standard can be expressed in terms of a detectability index d_a derived from an ROC (receiver operating characteristic) curve. The efficiency is then defined as

$$\eta = \frac{d_a^2(\text{human observer})}{d_a^2(\text{standard observer})}. \tag{1}$$

Most of the research reported in this volume will focus on the numerator in an efficiency expression; we look at the denominator. If the objective of the perceptual study is to quantify human performance relative to the best achievable performance, the denominator observer should be an ideal observer, but we have two choices for which ideal observer to use.

By definition, the absolute ideal observer is one who has full knowledge of the statistical properties of the data and uses it to optimize d_a, Bayes risk or some other measure of performance. It is well known [1, 2] that this oberver computes the likelihood ratio (or its logarithm) and compares it to a threshold in order to make a decision. We shall refer to it as the Bayesian ideal observer.

---

[*] Also with Optical Sciences Center, Univ. of Arizona
[†] Also with Program in Applied Mathematics, Univ. of Arizona

The difficulty with the Bayesian ideal observer is that it has not been analytically tractable except for a few stylized problems, such as detection of a known signal on a nonrandom background. This problem, referred to as SKE/BKE (signal known exactly, background known exactly), is not very representative of clinical detection problems, but it does lead to a simple form for the ideal observer. For SKE/BKE detection in Gaussian noise, the logarithm of the likelihood ratio is a linear functional of the image data, and it can be computed by laying a simple template (some form of matched filter) over the image and integrating. In more realistic problems, with random signals and/or backgrounds or with non-Gaussian noise, the log-likelihood ratio is nonlinear and difficult to compute.

Recent work [3, 4, 5] has significantly extended the range of problems for which we can compute the performance of the Bayesian ideal observer, but in this paper we consider the ideal linear observer, also called the Hotelling observer [6, 7, 8, 9]. The Hotelling observer computes a linear functional of the data which, unlike the simple matched filter, takes into account randomness in the signal or background. We shall refer to this functional as the Hotelling test statistic.

The Hotelling observer is optimal among linear observers in the sense that it maximizes a signal-to-noise ratio (SNR) called the Hotelling trace, defined more precisely in the next section. The Hotelling observer cannot be guaranteed to be optimal, even among linear observers, in terms of d_a or other measures derived from an ROC curve; the Hotelling trace is equivalent to d_a only if the test statistic is normally distributed. In practice, however, a linear combination of data values, such as the Hotelling test statistic or any other linear discriminant, will probably be normally distributed as a result of the central-limit theorem. If all linear observers yield normally distributed test statistics, then Hotelling is also the optimal linear observer in the d_a sense.

Since the Hotelling test statistic is an optimal linear discriminant, one might associate it with the well-known Fisher linear discriminant, but we wish to preserve an important distinction: the Fisher discriminant is the best you can do (in an SNR sense) if all you have available are sample data sets (images in our case), while the Hotelling observer is defined fundamentally as an ensemble or population quantity. The performance of a Fisher discriminant is a random variable, dependent on the particular training set of images used, while the Hotelling trace is a nonrandom quantity characteristic of an infinite population. As discussed in Sec. 2.4, it is often possible to compute the Hotelling trace from first principles without resort to sample images at all.

Analytical calculations of the Hotelling trace require analytical models of the images, or at least the ability to simulate many noise-free images. The calculations can be improved by developing more realistic models or simulation codes, but one can never be sure how applicable the results are to real clinical images. In this paper, therefore, we consider the use of sample clinical images to *estimate* the ensemble Hotelling trace. The estimate is, of course, a random variable, and we must investigate its statistical properties, but it is still distinct from any sort of performance measure that could be derived from the Fisher discriminant[*].

The objective of this paper is thus to develop techniques for estimation of the Hotelling trace and the template used to compute the Hotelling test statistic. The estimates are essentially maximum likelihood, but prior knowledge of the form of the template is built in through choice of the representation used for it. For simplicity, only signal-detection tasks with a nonrandom signal are considered, but the methods can be extended to random signals as well.

Section 2 reviews the basic idea of the Hotelling observer and explains the limitations of both analytic and direct-estimation approaches. Section 3 then details a new approach which attempts to balance computational feasibility with clinical realism. Section 4 presents some preliminary experiments to demonstrate the new approach.

2. THE HOTELLING OBSERVER

2.1. Definitions and basic concepts

Signal detection is a form of binary hypothesis testing where the null hypothesis H_0 is that the signal is absent and the alternative hypothesis H_1 is that it is present. The data available for performing this task are a

---

[*]To add to the semantic confusion, one performance measure that could be associated with the Fisher discriminant is the Hotelling T^2 statistic. The Hotelling trace, as we use the term, is the expectation value of T^2 if the image data are multivariate normal.

set of pixel values $\{g_m, m = 1,..., M\}$, which we can order as an $M \times 1$ vector $\mathbf{g}$. For deciding between H_0 and H_1, the Hotelling observer computes a scalar test statistic θ which is linear in $\mathbf{g}$ and can therefore be written as

$$\theta = \sum_{m=1}^{M} w_m g_m = \mathbf{w}^t \mathbf{g} , \qquad (2)$$

where $\mathbf{w}$ is an $M \times 1$ vector of weights $\{w_m\}$ and the superscript t denotes transpose. If θ is greater than some threshold θ_{th}, the observer decides that H_1 is true, and if $\theta < \theta_{th}$ it decides that H_0 is true.

If signal-present and signal-absent images are equally likely to occur, the Hotelling template $\mathbf{w}$ is given by [6, 7]

$$\mathbf{w} = [\tfrac{1}{2}\mathbf{K}_1 + \tfrac{1}{2}\mathbf{K}_2]^{-1}(\bar{\mathbf{g}}_2 - \bar{\mathbf{g}}_1) , \qquad (3)$$

where $\mathbf{K}_j$ is the covariance matrix of $\mathbf{g}$ under hypothesis j and $\bar{\mathbf{g}}_j$ is the corresponding mean vector.

The expression in (3) simplifies somewhat if we consider SKE detection of a specified signal on a random background, where the background is described by an $M \times 1$ random vector $\mathbf{b}$. The signal-present hypothesis H_1 is that $\mathbf{g} = \mathbf{b} + \mathbf{s}$, where $\mathbf{s}$ is a nonrandom $M \times 1$ signal vector, and H_0 is that $\mathbf{g} = \mathbf{b}$. For this problem, $\bar{\mathbf{g}}_2 - \bar{\mathbf{g}}_1 = \mathbf{s}$. Moreover, if the noise is independent of the signal, then $\mathbf{K}_1 = \mathbf{K}_2 \equiv \mathbf{K}$. Even if the noise is Poisson and hence signal dependent in principle, we can still say that $\mathbf{K}_1 \simeq \mathbf{K}_2$ if the signal has low contrast and makes a small change in the mean data. Thus we have, for an SKE problem,

$$\mathbf{w} = \mathbf{K}^{-1}\mathbf{s} . \qquad (4)$$

It must be stressed that the data covariance matrix $\mathbf{K}$ includes the effects of both background randomness (anatomical noise) and Poisson or other measurement noise. In previous papers [6, 7, 10] we have related $\mathbf{K}$ to the autocovariance function of the objects before imaging and to the properties of an imaging system, but here we regard it as a property of the image data without worrying too much about how it got there.

Similarly, the signal is specified as a property of the image data, and a subsidiary calculation is needed if we want to compute how a specified lesion in the actual object transforms to a signal vector in the data. Alternatively, if an actual imaging system is available, we can measure a low-noise image of some object of interest without any background; if the system is linear, this image can be multiplied by a scalar to get the required $\mathbf{s}$.

2.2. Figures of merit

One way to specify how well any observer can distinguish between H_0 and H_1 is to use an SNR defined by

$$\text{SNR}_\theta^2 \equiv \frac{[\langle\theta\rangle_1 - \langle\theta\rangle_0]^2}{\tfrac{1}{2}\text{var}_1(\theta) + \tfrac{1}{2}\text{var}_0(\theta)} , \qquad (5)$$

where θ is the test statistic used by the observer, $\langle\theta\rangle_j$ denotes the conditional expectation of θ given that H_j is true and $\text{var}_j(\cdot)$ denotes the corresponding conditional variance.

If θ is normally distributed under both hypotheses, SNR_θ is related to the area under the ROC curve (denoted AUC) by

$$\text{AUC} = \frac{1}{2} + \frac{1}{2}\text{erf}\left(\frac{\text{SNR}_\theta}{2}\right), \qquad (6)$$

where $\text{erf}(\cdot)$ is the error function. Thus, in this case there is a simple monotonic relation between AUC and SNR_θ, so it doesn't matter which we adopt as a figure of merit.

The detectability index d_a is defined by

$$d_a \equiv 2\,\mathrm{erf}^{-1}(2\mathrm{AUC} - 1)\,, \tag{7}$$

where $\mathrm{erf}^{-1}(\cdot)$ is the inverse of the error function.

For the specific case of the Hotelling observer, SNR_θ^2 is denoted SNR_{Hot}^2; from (2) and (4), it is straight-forward to show that

$$\mathrm{SNR}_{Hot}^2 = \mathbf{s}^t\,\mathbf{K}^{-1}\mathbf{s}\,. \tag{8}$$

This expression can also be written as

$$\mathrm{SNR}_{Hot}^2 = \mathrm{tr}[\mathbf{K}^{-1}\mathbf{s}\mathbf{s}^t]\,, \tag{9}$$

where $\mathbf{s}\mathbf{s}^t$ is the outer product of $\mathbf{s}$ with itself, hence an $M \times M$ matrix, and tr denotes the trace or sum of diagonal elements of a matrix. Though it involves a trace, (9) is not quite equal to the Hotelling trace J as defined in our previous papers. If signal-present and signal-absent images are equally probable, as we shall assume throughout this paper, the relation is simply $J = \frac{1}{4}\mathrm{SNR}_{Hot}^2$.

If the Hotelling test statistic is normally distributed (even if the data vector $\mathbf{g}$ is not), then d_a^2 and SNR_{Hot}^2 are identical.

2.3. Covariance estimation

The expressions above for θ and J involve the $M \times M$ pixel covariance matrix $\mathbf{K}$. In the SKE/BKE problem, where the only randomness in $\mathbf{g}$ comes from the measurement noise, $\mathbf{K}$ is the noise covariance matrix, which is usually known from the physics of the imaging system. With clinical images, however, $\mathbf{K}$ includes ana-tomical or patient-structured noise and is not known.

The Fisher discriminant could be constructed as an approximation to the Hotelling discriminant if we could estimate $\mathbf{K}$ from sample images, but the sheer size of $\mathbf{K}$ makes this approach impossible in practice. If we consider an $N \times N$ image, then the number of pixels is $M = N^2$, so $\mathbf{K}$ is an $N^2 \times N^2$ matrix. If we estimate it by collecting N_s sample images and forming the sample covariance matrix $\mathcal{K}$, we must have N_s at least equal to N^2 in order for $\mathcal{K}$ to be nonsingular, and we need N_s to be 10 to 100 times N^2 to get a stable estimate. Thus, even for small 64×64 images, we need, say, 40,000 - 400,000 images to compute the Fisher discriminant.

2.4. Analytic and quasi-analytic approaches

Because it is not practical to compute a Fisher discriminant on pixel values, efforts at the University of Arizona have concentrated instead on analytic and quasi-analytic computation of the Hotelling discriminant.

One useful model for which a fully analytical approach is feasible is the *lumpy background* introduced by Rolland [8, 11]. This model is an important advance over the SKE/BKE problem since it includes background randomness, but it is analytically tractable since the background is a stationary random process with a computable autocorrelation function.

A lumpy background can be generated either by superimposing blobs of known profile at random loca-tions or by filtering of white noise. This background can then be imaged (in a computer) through an arbitrary imaging system, measurement noise can be added, and various post-processing algorithms, including linear or nonlinear tomographic reconstruction [12, 13] can be applied. The resulting images show some of the charac-teristics of real medical images, but of course they are not anatomically accurate. They have been used for many psychophysical studies at Arizona [7, 8, 11-15].

A simple special case of the lumpy background is what Burgess calls *two-component noise* [16], which is identical to what Rolland called a Type 2 lumpy background [11]. In this case, a low-frequency component is generated by filtering white Gaussian noise, and then a white-noise Gaussian component is added to the result. No specific imaging system is modeled and there is no post-processing or image reconstruction. These Type 2 or two-component images are useful as stimuli for psychophysical studies but there is no specific relation to imaging systems. Moreover, they are constructed as Gaussian random processes so they give no way of studying the effect of deviations from Gaussian statistics. By contrast, lumpy backgrounds generated by superimposing blobs (Type 1) may be decidedly non-Gaussian [14, 15, 17].

Though lumpy backgrounds have proven fruitful for investigating human perception [7, 8, 11, 14-18] and optimizing reconstruction algorithms [12, 13], they are nevertheless only a rough approximation to the random backgrounds encountered clinically. It was recognized early in our investigations of the Hotelling observer that it was also possible to simulate clinically realistic objects and to compute the Hotelling trace in a hybrid fashion, combining analytical methods with simulated sample images. The theory behind this approach is detailed by Fiete *et al.* [7]. It was applied successfully to images generated by an accurate simulation of the liver [19, 20].

Fiete's method relies on the ability to generate anatomically accurate sample images without measurement noise. The covariance matrix of the measurement noise (usually Poisson) can be computed analytically. Since the measurement noise is usually uncorrelated with the anatomy (though not necessarily statistically independent), the overall covariance matrix can be written rigorously as

$$ \mathbf{K} = \mathbf{K}^{anat} + \mathbf{K}^{noise} , \tag{10} $$

where $\mathbf{K}^{anat}$ is the covariance due to anatomical variations only and $\mathbf{K}^{noise}$ is the covariance matrix of the measurement noise. If the data vector $\mathbf{g}$ is a raw image, without any post-processing or image reconstruction, then $\mathbf{K}^{noise}$ is a diagonal matrix. If the noise is Poisson, the diagonal elements are equal to the means of components of $\mathbf{g}$. If a post-processing algorithm is used, $\mathbf{K}^{noise}$ can be computed, even for nonlinear algorithms [13, 21, 22].

Fiete's approach is to estimate $\mathbf{K}^{anat}$ from simulated, noise-free sample images, compute $\mathbf{K}^{noise}$ essentially analytically (though with the means estimated from samples in the Poisson case) and then to invert the resulting estimate of $\mathbf{K}$ to get $\mathbf{w}$ and J. He was able to work with as few as 64 sample images, but only because he was able to get the images before addition of measurement noise.

3. USE OF SAMPLE CLINICAL IMAGES

In this section we develop a strategy for estimation of Hotelling performance when we have no analytical model for the anatomical variations and no access to images without measurement noise. The basic problem we must overcome in this case is the dimensionality problem -- the size of a pixel covariance matrix is huge compared to the number of sample images we can hope to collect.

3.1. Choice of signal

Although SKE/BKE detection problems can be very misleading since they do not account for anatomical or patient-structured noise, exactly known signals are very useful. For one thing, it is useful to be able to discuss detectability as a function of signal size and profile. We can ask: If the signal is a blob of specified profile and size, and if we know its location, what is the detectability? If we have a mathematical (as opposed to psychophysical) answer to that question, we can plot the detectability as a function of size, contrast, location or other signal parameters.

The Hotelling formalism does allow arbitrary signal variability, but it is simplest for SKE problems. Moreover, in many cases the Hotelling trace for random signals can be derived from knowledge of it with fixed signals. For example, if the signal can be present in one of L non-overlapping locations with equal probablility, and if the background statistics are the same at all locations, then the trace is just $1/L$ times the trace for an SKE signal at one location [20].

In real clinical images, there may be important variations in detectability of a lesion depending on where it is located, and we have two options in such cases. We can either compute the SKE Hotelling trace for different anatomical locations, or we can compute an average trace over all locations. We have referred to the latter option as signal-known exactly-but random (SKER) [23, 24]. It corresponds to a psychophysical experiment in which the signal can be at a random location but where a cross hair or other cue identifies to the observer the location of the possible signal.

The SKER paradigm offers two advantages in practice. If the signal locations are uniformly distributed over the image field, the background is effectively stationary and the analytical expression for average Hotelling trace takes a simple form in a Fourier-series representation. In this case there is an intimate relation between average detectability and the Fourier cross-talk matrix [24-26].

The other advantage of SKER relates to sample images and does not require the assumption that all locations are equally probable. If we can estimate J at each of L points in N_s sample images, then the overall sample size is LN_s, so one image is equivalent to L background samples.

3.2. Channels

To estimate the Hotelling trace from samples, it is necessary to reduce the size of the sample covariance matrix. In essence, this means that we must work with some functions of the pixel values rather than with the original pixel values themselves. In the pattern-recognition literature, the functions are called *features*, and the transformation from pixels to features is called *feature extraction*. If the functions are linear transformations of the data vector, they are called linear features. A linear discriminant is a scalar-valued linear combination of linear features. Much of the art of pattern recognition is in choosing features that optimize our ability to classify the patterns.

We focus in this paper on linear features but use a language that is more familiiar in the medical-imaging and perception communities; we shall speak in terms of *channels*, but in a very general sense, not necessarily the visual channels. We define a channel as any template $\mathbf{t}_k$ of the same size as an image (though many elements may be zero), and the *channel output* is any linear functional of the data $\mathbf{g}$ in the form,

$$y_k = \mathbf{t}_k^t \mathbf{g} = \sum_{m=1}^{M} t_{km} g_m .$$
(11)

Hence a channel output is same thing as a linear feature in pattern recognition. If there are K channels, then each image $\mathbf{g}$ yields a set of K numbers $\{y_k\}$ or a $K \times 1$ feature vector $\mathbf{y}$, given explicitly by

$$\mathbf{y} = \mathbf{T}\mathbf{g} ,$$
(12)

where $\mathbf{T}$ is a $K \times M$ matrix with elements t_{km}.

The optimal linear discriminant given access to only the channel outputs is the Hotelling observer in channel space. That is, the optimal discriminant function θ_c (where subscript c indicates channel) is given by [*cf.* (2)]

$$\theta_c = \sum_{k=1}^{K} w_{ck} y_k = \mathbf{w}_c^t \mathbf{y} ,$$
(13)

where $\mathbf{w}_c$ is a $K \times 1$ vector of weights $\{w_{ck}\}$. Specifically, for an SKE problem, $\mathbf{w}_c$ is given by [*cf.* (4)]

$$\mathbf{w}_c = \mathbf{K}_c^{-1} \mathbf{s}_c ,$$
(14)

where $\mathbf{K}_c$ is the $K \times K$ covariance matrix of the channel outputs, given by

$$\mathbf{K}_c = \mathbf{T}\mathbf{K}\mathbf{T}^t ,$$
(15)

and $\mathbf{s}_c$ is the signal as seen through the channels, *i.e.*,

$$\mathbf{s}_c = \mathbf{T}\mathbf{s} \; . \tag{16}$$

The Hotelling trace on the channel outputs is

$$J_c = \tfrac{1}{4}\mathbf{s}_c^t \mathbf{K}_c^{-1}\mathbf{s}_c \; . \tag{17}$$

If $K \ll M$, the use of channels leads to a large reduction in dimensionality. Only K images are needed to get a nonsingular estimate of $\mathbf{K}_c$ and 10-100 times this number will give an excellent one.

3.3. When are the channels sufficient?

If we are given a set of channels $\{\mathbf{t}_k\}$ and an adequate training set of clinical images, we can estimate J_c. But if our goal is to estimate J, we need to choose the channels so that $J_c \simeq J$. If that condition is satisfied, the channel outputs will serve as well as the pixel values themselves for performing the given signal-detection task. In the language of statistical decision theory, $\mathbf{y}$ is a *sufficient statistic* for the task if $J_c = J$.

A necessary and sufficient condition for $\mathbf{y}$ to be a sufficient statistic is that it be possible to synthesize the original Hotelling template $\mathbf{w}$ as a linear combination of the channel templates $\{\mathbf{t}_k\}$. Suppose we can write

$$\mathbf{w} = \sum_{k=1}^{K} a_k \mathbf{t}_k = \mathbf{T}^t \mathbf{a} \tag{18}$$

for some $K \times 1$ vector $\mathbf{a}$. Then the Hotelling test statistic is given by

$$\theta = \mathbf{w}^t \mathbf{g} = \mathbf{a}^t \mathbf{T}\mathbf{g} = \mathbf{a}^t \mathbf{y} \; . \tag{19}$$

Since the last form is a linear combination of the channel outputs, they are all we need to know to compute θ. It can also be shown that $\theta_c = \theta$ in this case, and that J_c is necessarily less than J if (18) cannot be satisfied.

3.4. Some possible choices for channels

One possible choice for the channels is pixels; we can get a dimensionality reduction just by looking at a restricted field of view, using a subset of the entire image [20, 27]. For example, if we choose a 9×9 window centered on a known signal location, $K = 81$ and a few hundred to a few thousand images are adequate for estimating J_c. The only problem is that it may be difficult to establish that the pixel values in the small window constitute a sufficient statistic. Image correlations may be long range, and even if they are short range, $\mathbf{K}^{-1}$ may be long range.

A similar idea can be applied in the Fourier domain. The discrete Fourier transform (DFT) of $\mathbf{g}$ is another $M \times 1$ vector, denoted $\mathbf{G}$, and we can express the Hotelling test statistic as

$$\theta = \mathbf{W}^\dagger \mathbf{G} \; , \tag{20}$$

where $\mathbf{W}$ is the DFT of $\mathbf{w}$ and $\dagger$ denotes adjoint (complex conjugate of the transpose). The template in the Fourier domain is also $M \times 1$, but if we know that the signal is essentially limited to small band, we can retain only a subset of frequencies and thereby get a dimensionality reduction [28].

Again, however, it is difficult to establish that there is no loss of detectability as a result of the band-limiting. We know from Rolland's work on lumpy backgrounds that the Hotelling observer will look at rather high spatial frequencies, especially if the measurement noise is low, so bandwidth restriction may be dangerous.

A very interesting option is to let nature choose the channels for us. It is well established through psychophysical and electrophysiological studies that humans process visual information through spatial-frequency-selective channels, and there is at least rough agreement on the form and bandwidth of the channel templates. A number of researchers have used similar templates for feature extraction when the goal was machine-based pattern recognition rather than explaining perceptual studies. For example, Hutton and Strickland [32] have recently used channels akin to the cortex transform [30] to extract features. They validated their results against the lumpy-background model where J was known.

The problem with anthropomorphic channels is that the human is known to be markedly suboptimal relative to Hotelling in high-pass (*e.g.* tomographic) noise [33, 34]. Anthropomorphic channels are an obvious choice when the goal is to predict human performance, but they may not be if the goal is to estimate ideal performance.

3.5. General considerations in channel selection

The problem of estimating the Hotelling template has a lot in common with image reconstruction. Consider an object described by an $N \times 1$ vector $\mathbf{f}$ and an imaging system described by a known $M \times N$ matrix $\mathbf{H}$. The data vector is given by

$$\mathbf{g} = \mathbf{Hf} + \mathbf{n} , \tag{21}$$

where $\mathbf{n}$ is an unknown $M \times 1$ noise vector, the statistics of which can depend on $\mathbf{f}$. To cast the Hotelling problem in the same form, we first rewrite (4) as

$$\mathbf{s} = \mathbf{Kw} , \tag{22}$$

but since we don't know $\mathbf{K}$, we approximate it with the sample covariance $\mathcal{K}$ and write

$$\mathbf{s} = \mathcal{K}\mathbf{w} + \epsilon , \tag{23}$$

where ϵ is an error term given by

$$\epsilon = \mathbf{Kw} - \mathcal{K}\mathbf{w} . \tag{24}$$

The analogy between (21) and (23) is strong: $\mathbf{g}$ and $\mathbf{s}$ are known vectors, $\mathbf{H}$ and $\mathcal{K}$ are known matrices, $\mathbf{f}$ and $\mathbf{w}$ are the vectors ("objects") we wish to determine, and $\mathbf{n}$ and ϵ are unknown, possibly object-dependent, error terms.

The analogy persists if we attempt a direct solution of (21) or (23). We could attempt to operate on both sides of (21) with an inverse or pseudoinverse of $\mathbf{H}$, and similarly to operate on both sides of (23) with an inverse or pseudoinverse of $\mathcal{K}$, but in both cases the result would be disastrous. The error terms would be amplified by components of $\mathbf{H}$ or $\mathcal{K}$ corresponding to small singular values or eigenvalues, and the estimates of $\mathbf{f}$ or $\mathbf{w}$ would be very noisy and unphysical.

The solution, in template estimation as well as image reconstruction, is to make use of prior information. We usually know *a priori* that objects and Hotelling templates are smooth, in some sense, and it is essential that we regularize the problem by enforcing smoothness.

One way to enforce smoothness is through choice of the representation of the unknown quantity. In image reconstruction, for example, we are free to choose the grid size and expansion functions used in approximating a continuous object with a discrete vector. Hanson and Wecksung [35] have discussed the use of Gaussians and other smooth functions for this purpose, and Lewitt [36] has proposed and analyzed a set of compact, smooth functions called Kaiser-Bessel functions. If the set of functions used to represent the unknown is smooth, the estimate of the unknown will be smooth.

Often we will have additional prior knowledge. In image processing with incoherent objects, we know that the object cannot be negative, and we should enforce that condition in the reconstruction algorithm. Hotelling templates, on the other hand, do have negative values, so we cannot use a positivity constraint, but we can take advantage of the fact that we are considering SKE tasks. That means that the template will have a positive value at the known location of the signal and that it will fall off and eventually go negative as we move away from that location.

We might also know that the template is an even function or a rotationally symmetric one (if both the signal and the background covariance are rotationally symmetric). This information, too, can be built in by appropriate choice of the representation for **w**.

Our proposed general approach, therefore, is to represent the unknown Hotelling template **w** as a finite series of smooth, and possibly symmetric, functions centered on the signal location; then we attempt to estimate the coefficients in the expansion.

3.6. Laguerre-Gauss functions

The specific smooth functions we study in this paper are the Laguerre-Gauss functions, products of Laguerre polynomials and Gaussians. The Laguerre polynomials are defined by

$$L_n(x) = \sum_{m=0}^{n} (-1)^m \begin{pmatrix} n \\ m \end{pmatrix} \frac{x^m}{m!} .$$ (25)

The first few polynomials are:

$$L_0(x) = 1 , \quad L_1(x) = -x + 1 , \quad L_2(x) = \frac{1}{2!}(x^2 - 4x + 2)$$

$$L_3(x) = \frac{1}{3!}(-x^3 + 9x^2 - 18x + 6) , \quad L_4(x) = \frac{1}{4!}(x^4 - 16x^3 + 72x^2 - 96x + 24) .$$ (26)

The Laguerre polynomials are orthonormal on $(0, \infty)$ with respect to an exponential weight factor:

$$\int_0^\infty dx \ e^{-x} L_n(x) L_m(x) = \delta_{nm} .$$ (27)

The change of variables $x = 2\pi r^2 / a^2$ yields a new orthonormal family satisfying

$$\int_0^\infty r dr \ u_n(r) u_m(r) = \delta_{nm} ,$$ (28)

where

$$u_n(r) \equiv \frac{2\sqrt{\pi}}{a} \exp(-\pi r^2 / a^2) L_n(2\pi r^2 / a^2) .$$ (29)

A possible expansion for the template, expressed in continuous polar coordinates with origin at the signal location, is

$$w(r, \theta) = \sum_n \sum_m \alpha_{nm} \exp(-\pi r^2 / a^2) L_n(2\pi r^2 / a^2) e^{im\theta} .$$ (30)

This expansion is sufficiently general to allow representation of any function of r and θ that is square integrable over the plane with a Gaussian weight. If we can assume that the signal and covariance are rotationally symmetric, we can consider just the $m = 0$ term in (30).

The final digital template **w** is obtained by sampling $w(r, \theta)$ on the pixel grid.

4. RESULTS

We have carried out two sets of experiments to demonstrate the usefulness of the Laguerre-Gauss representation of the Hotelling template. The first set used Rolland's Type 1 lumpy backgrounds, where we knew the true template and the true value of J. The second set used digitized coronary angiograms with artificially generated signals. In both cases, the template considered had the form of a sampled version of (30) with $m = 0$ and $n = 0,..., 5$. There were thus just six coefficients to estimate.

The lumpy-background experiments were similar to the work of Hutton and Strickland [32] on channelized detection filters, the main difference being in the choice of channels. The images were generated by randomly selecting K locations in the field, where K is a Poisson random variable with mean $\overline{K}$. A Gaussian blob of amplitude A_b and standard deviation σ_b was then centered on each selected location, and the resulting grey levels were summed over blobs to give a lumpy background pattern. This pattern was imaged through a simulated pinhole imaging system with a Gaussian point spread function of standard deviation σ_p to give a noise-free image, which was then used as input to a Poisson random-number generator. The ratio of background or anatomical noise to Poisson noise was controlled by the exposure time in the simulated pinhole imaging system. The signal, when present, was a Gaussian of standard deviation σ_s superimposed on the lumpy background and passed through the same simulated imaging system. (Note carefully that the terms *Gaussian* and *standard deviation* in this paragraph refer to spatial distributions, not statistical ones.)

The study used 2000 simulated images. The partial templates corresponding to each term in the Laguerre-Gauss expansion (see Fig. 1) were applied to each image at the known signal location, thereby generating a feature vector with 6 components for each image. The process was repeated for four exposure times, 0.01, 50, 250 and 750 sec. For the shortest time, Poisson noise dominated, while the anatomical or lumpy-background noise dominated for the longest time. The pixel grey levels at the longer times were not normally distributed, perhaps being closer to log-normal, though this point was not investigated in detail. The features themselves appeared to be close to normal; a representative set of histograms of the sample outputs is shown in Fig. 2.

A great advantage of the lumpy backgrounds is that we can compute the Hotelling template analytically. Figs. 2 and 3 compare analytic templates to ones computed from the Laguerre-Gauss series with coefficients estimated by $\alpha = \mathcal{K}_c^{-1} s_c$. The visual agreement appears to be excellent.

A more quantitative comparison was obtained by computing the performance of the estimated template and comparing it to the theoretical performance. A two-alternative forced-choice experiment was performed in which every simulated signal-present image was compared to every signal-absent one. The fraction of correct classifications in this comparison was identified with AUC, and then d_a was computed from (7). Results obtained are summarized in Table 1. In all cases, the d_a computed from the estimated template agrees closely with the theoretical value.

TABLE 1

Exposure time	Theoretical d_a	d_a from samples
750 s	3.61	3.62
250 s	3.59	3.47
50 s	3.59	3.53
0.01 s	3.13	3.14

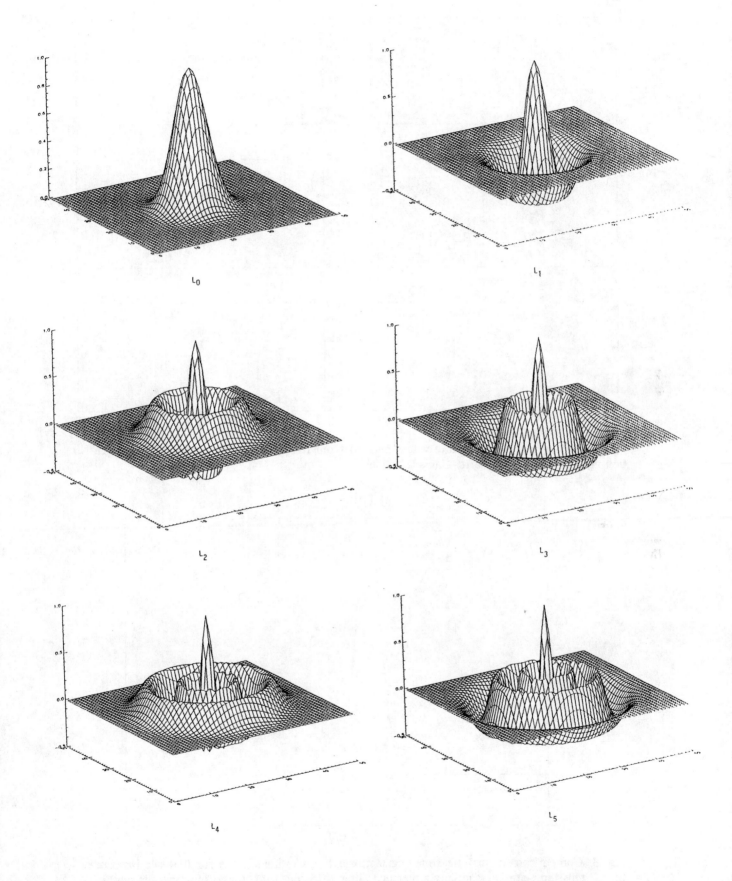

Fig. 1. Illustration of the Laguerre-Gauss expansion functions, corresponding to $n = 0,..., 5$, $m = 0$ in (30).

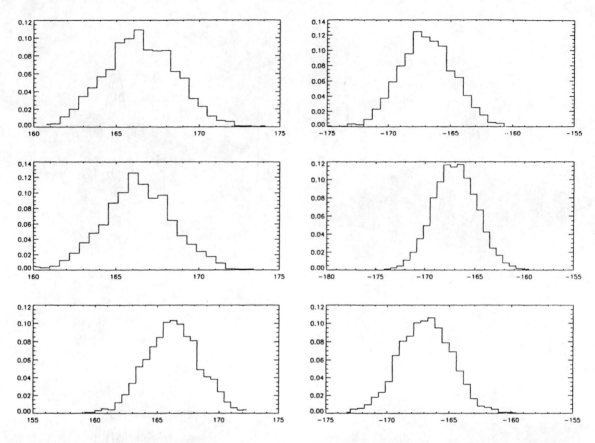

Fig. 2. Histogram of the feature values derived from lumpy-background images by integration against a single Laguerre-Gauss function.

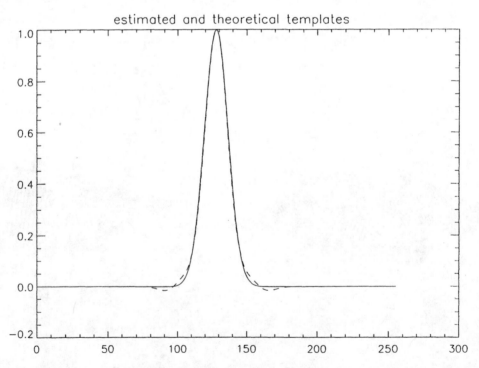

Fig. 3. Comparison of analytic Hotelling template to an estimated one for 0.01 sec exposure time. This template is essentially a matched filter since the background lumpiness is negligible in this limit and the measurement noise is white.

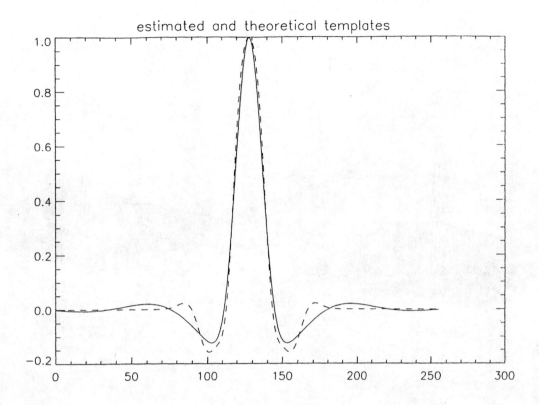

Fig. 4. Comparison of analytic Hotelling template to an estimated one for 750 sec exposure time. This template now has negative sidelobes which serve to estimate and subtract off the anatomical noise.

The second set of experiments used digitized coronary angiograms from Cedars Sinai Medical Center. The images were acquired at 30 frames/sec with a 7" Dia. image intensifier (Advantx/DXC, General Electric Medical Systems). Imaging parameters included standard automatic exposure control at 30 μGy per frame and extended-dynamic-range video circuitry. Digital images were obtained with a linear analog amplifier and lookup table to achieve a 512×512 image (0.3 mm per pixel) with 256 gray levels. All digital spatial filters were disabled. Rectangular subregions of size 256×128 pixels were extracted as test images for this study. A total of 500 different images were sampled from 50 coronary angiograms.

The signal in this study was a hemi-ellipsoid that mimics an arterial filling defect (thrombus). The signal was blurred with a Gaussian point spread function and added to the angiogram images.

The same procedure as for the lumpy backgrounds was used to derive a six-dimensional vector of channel outputs. Histograms of these outputs were quite similar to those shown in Fig. 2. The template, estimated as before, is shown in Fig. 5, along with the signal for comparison. The d_a for this template was computed and compared to d_a obtained by selecting a 12×12 subset of the image and using pixel values as the channel outputs. Results of this comparison will be presented orally at the conference.

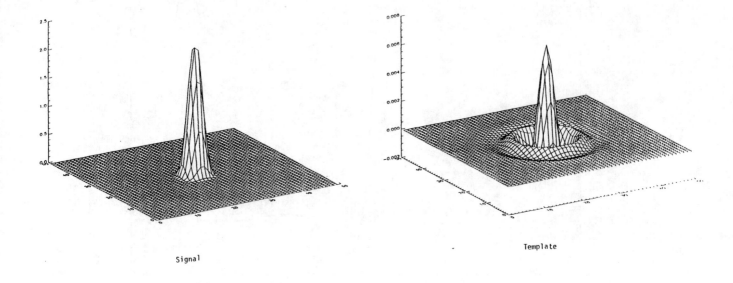

Fig. 5. Left: signal to be detected. Right: Hotelling template estimated from samples. Note the similarity to the template depicted in Fig. 4 for the lumpy background.

5. SUMMARY AND CONCLUSIONS

The main point of this paper has been that estimation of a Hotelling template for an SKE problem has much in common with standard problems in image reconstruction. In both cases, noisy data can lead to very rough, noisy images unless some regularization or stabilization is employed. The specific stabilization suggested here was to represent the template as a linear combination of a small number of smooth basis functions such as Laguerre-Gauss functions. The analogous procedure in image reconstruction is to represent the object as a superposition of smooth blobs such as Gaussians [35] or Kaiser-Bessel functions [36].

We refer to the smooth functions as channels, though they may not have anything to do with the channels in the visual system. A finite set of channel outputs will be a sufficient statistic for a given detection problem if and only if the Hotelling template can be expressed as a linear combination of the channel functions. Under these conditions, the Hotelling trace based on the channel outputs will be the same as the Hotelling trace based on the original image data.

The particular channel functions introduced here are the Laguerre-Gauss functions. In studies with the lumpy backgrounds, excellent agreement was found between templates and d_a values estimated from samples and the corresponding theoretical quantities. In studies with clinical images, the histograms of channel outputs and the estimated Hotelling templates were found to be quite similar to the ones obtained with the lumpy background. These findings suggest that the lumpy background may accurately capture the key features of real anatomical backgrounds, at least for simple signal detection.

Future research will relax the isotropy assumption, for example by using elliptical blobs in the lumpy background. It will also investigate the stability of the estimates as a function of the number of radial terms in the template expansion, the number of angular terms, the number of samples and the blob profile. We also plan to study basis functions other than Laguerre-Gauss.

ACKNOWLEDGEMENTS

The authors have benefitted from discussions with Kyle Myers, Robert Wagner and Eric Clarkson. This work was supported by the National Institutes of Health (NIH) through grant no. RO1 CA52643, but it does not represent an official position of NIH.

REFERENCES

1. H.L. Van Trees, *Detection, Estimation, and Modulation Theory*, Vol. *I* (John Wiley, New York, 1968).

2. J.L. Melsa and D.L. Cohn, *Decision and Estimation Theory* (McGraw Hill, New York, 1978).

3. H.H. Barrett and C.K. Abbey, "Bayesian detection of random signals on random backgrounds," XVth International Conference on Information Processing in Medical Imaging, published in Lecture Notes in Computer Science, Springer-Verlag, Berlin, 1997.

4. H.H. Barrett, C.K. Abbey and E. Clarkson, "Objective assessment of image quality III: ROC metrics, ideal observers and likelihood-generating functions", to be published in J. Opt. Soc. Am. *A*.

5. H.H. Barrett, C.K. Abbey and E. Clarkson, "Some unlikely properties of the likelihood ratio and its logarithm", Proc. SPIE 3340, 1998.

6. W.E. Smith and H.H. Barrett, "Hotelling trace criterion as a figure of merit for the optimization of imaging systems," J. Opt. Soc. Am. A, 3:717-725, 1986.

7. R.D. Fiete, H.H. Barrett, W.E. Smith and K.J. Myers "The Hotelling trace criterion and its correlation with human observer performance," J. Opt. Soc. Am. A., 4:945-953, 1987.

8. J.P. Rolland and H.H. Barrett, "Effect of random background inhomogeneity on observer detection performance," J. Opt. Soc. Am. A., 9(5):649-658, 1992.

9. K.J. Myers, J.P. Rolland, H.H. Barrett and R.F. Wagner, "Aperture optimization for emission imaging: effect of a spatially varying background," J. Opt. Soc. Am. A, 7:1279-1293, 1990.

10. H.H. Barrett, "Objective assessment of image quality: effects of quantum noise and object variability", J. Opt. Soc. Am. A, 7:1266-1278, 1990.

11. J.P. Rolland. University of Arizona. Ph. D. Dissertation. Factors influencing lesion detection in medical imaging, 1990.

12. C.K. Abbey, H.H. Barrett, and D.W. Wilson, "Observer signal-to-noise ratios for the ML-EM algorithm," Proc. SPIE 2712:47-58, 1996.

13. C.K. Abbey, H.H. Barrett and M. P. Eckstein, "Practical issues and methodology in assessment of image quality using model observers," Proc. SPIE 3032, 1997.

14. J. Yao and H.H. Barrett "Predicting Human Performance by a Channelized Hotelling Observer Model," SPIE Math. Methods Med. Imaging, 1768:161-168, 1992.

15. H.H. Barrett, J. Yao, J.P. Rolland, K.J. Myers, "Model observers for assessment of image quality", Proc. Nat. Acad. Sci. 90:9758-9765, 1993.

16. A.E. Burgess, X. Li, and C.K. Abbey, Visual signal detectability with two noise components: anomalous masking effects," J. Opt. Soc. Am. A 14(9):2420-2442, 1997.

17. B.D. Gallas and H.H. Barrett, "Detectability (ideal and human) for a lumpy background model as a function of background parameters", Optical Society of America, Annual Meeting, 1997.

18. A.E. Burgess, "Statistically defined backgrounds: Performance of a modified nonprewhitening matched filter model", J. Opt. Soc. Am. A 11:1237-1242, 1994.

19. E. Cargill. University of Arizona. Ph. D. Dissertation. A mathematical liver model and its application to system optimization and texture analysis, 1989.

20. H.H. Barrett, T.A. Gooley, K.A. Girodias, J.P. Rolland, T.A. White and J. Yao, "Linear discriminants and image quality," Image and Vision Computing 10(6), 451-460, 1992.

21. H.H. Barrett, D.W. Wilson and B.M.W. Tsui, "Noise properties of the EM algorithm: I Theory", Phys. Med. Biol. 39:833-846, 1994.

22. D.W. Wilson, B.M.W. Tsui and H.H. Barrett, "Noise properties of the EM algorithm: II Monte Carlo simulations", Phys. Med. Biol. 39:847-872, 1994.

23. H.H. Barrett, J.L. Denny, R.F. Wagner, and K.J. Myers, "Objective assessment of image quality. II Fisher information, Fourier crosstalk, and figures of merit for task performance," J. Opt. Soc. Am. A 12(5):834-852, 1995.

24. H.H. Barrett, J.L. Denny, H.C. Gifford, and C.K. Abbey, "Generalized NEQ: Fourier analysis where you would least expect to find it," Proc. SPIE 2708:41-52, 1996.

25. H.H. Barrett and H.C. Gifford, Cone-beam tomography with discrete data sets, Phys. Med. Biol. 39:451-476, 1994.

26. H. Gifford, University of Arizona. Ph. D. Dissertation. Theory and Application of Fourier Crosstalk: An Evaluator for Digital-System Design, 1997.

27. M.P. Eckstein and J.S. Whiting, "Lesion detection in structured noise", Acad. Radiol. 3:249-253, 1995.

28. R.M. Gagne and R.F. Wagner, "Prewhitening matched filter SNR: Practical imnplementation, estimate and bias reduction", Proc. SPIE 3336, 1998.

29. A.B. Watson, "Detection and recognition of simple spatial forms", in *Physical and Biological Processing of Images*, O. J. Sander and A. C. Sleigh, eds., Kluwer Academis press, Dordrecht, 1983.

30. A.B. Watson, "The Cortex transform: Rapid computation of simulated neural images", Compuer Graphics and Image processing 39(3): 311-327, 1987.

31. M.P. Eckstein, C.K. Abbey and J.S. Whiting, "Human *vs.* model observer performance in anatomic backgrounds", Proc. SPIE 3340, 1998.

32. D.A. Hutton and R.N. Strickland, "Channelized filters for detecting tumors in nuclear medical images, " Medical Imaging 1997, M.H. Loew and K.M. Hanson, Eds., Proc. SPIE 3034:457-466, Feb 1997.

33. K.J. Myers, H.H. Barrett, M.C. Borgstrom, D.D. Patton and G.W. Seeley, "Effect of noise correlation on detectability of disk signals in medical imaging," J. Opt. Soc. Am. A 2:1752-1759, 1985.

34. K.J. Myers and H.H. Barrett "Addition of a channel mechanism to the ideal-observer model," J. Opt. Soc. Am. A. 4:2447-2457, 1987.

35. K.M. Hanson and G.W. Wecksung, "Local basis-function approach to computed tomography", Appl. Opt. 24:4028-4039, 1985.

36. R. M. Lewitt, "Alternatives to voxels for image representation in iterative reconstruction algorithms", Phys. Med. Biol. 37:705-716, 1992.

The Effect of Local Background Anatomical Patterns on the Detection of Subtle Lung Nodules in Chest Radiographs

Ehsan Samei[1], Michael J. Flynn[1], William R. Eyler[1], Edward Peterson[2]

[1] Department of Diagnostic Radiology
Henry Ford Health System, Detroit, Michigan

[2] Department of Biostatistics and Research Epidemiology
Henry Ford Health System, Detroit, Michigan

ABSTRACT

Anatomical noise in chest radiography, created by the projection of anatomical features in the thorax such as ribs and pulmonary vessels, greatly influences the detection of subtle lung nodules in chest radiographs. Detection may be hindered by 1) the "global" statistical characteristics of the background in relation to the signal associated with the nodule, and/or 2) the interference of the "local" background pattern with the nodule signal. This investigation aimed at assessing the influence of the latter process in the detection of subtle lung nodules. Six 8 × 8 cm images were extracted from the lung regions of six digital chest radiographs of normal patients from our clinic. Simulated nodules emulating the radiographic characteristics of subtle tissue-equivalent lesions ranging in size from 3.2 to 6.4 mm were numerically superimposed on the images. For each of the six lung images, a set of thirty-one processed images were produced, six containing no nodule, and the remaining 25 containing single nodules of five different sizes placed at five different locations within 6 mm of the center. The variation in location allowed different local background patterns to overlay the nodules. An observer detection study was then performed using 14 experienced radiologists. The observer data were analyzed to determine the variation in detectability with nodule location for all five sizes of the nodules. The preliminary results indicate that the variation in detectability of a nodule due to the influence of its local background surroundings is equivalent to that caused by changing its CD product by a factor of 4.45 ($\sim$ 0.28 in A_z).

Keyword List: Diagnostic radiology, observer performance • Lung neoplasms, diagnosis • Lung, nodule • Lung, radiography • Nodule detection studies

1 INTRODUCTION

Chest radiography is the most common diagnostic tool used to detect lung nodules.[1] Approximately 40% of lung nodules are manifestations of either primary lung cancer or metastatic disease.[2] Lung cancer is known to be the second leading cause of death in the United States, with approximately 150,000 deaths annually.[3] Statistical studies show that the five-year survival rate can be improved from an average of 13% to 46% if the disease is diagnosed early.[3,4] However, currently about 30% of lung nodules in chest radiographs are missed at first reading, even though they can be clearly identified if viewed retrospectively.[1,5] In spite of many technological advancements in chest radiography in the last few decades, this figure has not been improved.[6,7]

The detection of abnormalities in medical images is generally understood to be limited by the amount of noise in the image. In chest radiographs, noise can be differentiated into two major components: radiographic noise (mottle) and anatomical noise. For current chest radiographic systems, the single most important contributer to radiographic noise is the patient dose-limited quantum noise associated with the finite number of x-ray quanta used to form the image. The influence of quantum noise in the detection of low-contrast lesions in medical images is well understood.[8,9] For a given entrance exposure to the patient, the influence of quantum noise can be minimized by improving the detective quantum efficiency (DQE) of the imaging system. Many technical advancements in the past have focused on improving the DQE of the image receptor. Although this has led to general improvement in the image quality, observer performance studies have shown no improvement in the detection rate of lung lesions in chest radiographs in the last four decades.[6,7]

The second component of noise that can influence the detectability of low-contrast objects, object variability or anatomical noise, is less well understood.[10,11] In chest radiography, anatomical noise is a highly "correlated" noise pattern which greatly influences the detection of pulmonary nodules.[12–15] It is formed by the projection of anatomical features in the thorax such as ribs, pulmonary vessels, and lung tissue. In the past, insufficient research has been performed to understand the processes that contribute to this influence.

In a previous study, we measured the detectability of tissue-equivalent nodules in background images of radiographic mottle only and of radiographic mottle plus anatomical noise by means of two observer performance experiments.[16] For equivalent detection, nodules in anatomical background noise were at least an order of magnitude larger in contrast-diameter product than those in radiographic noise backgrounds (Figure 1). These results show that anatomical noise is a much more significant factor in the detection of subtle lung nodules than is radiographic noise, and that its influence merits further investigation.

The influence of anatomical noise on the detection of lung nodules may be considered at two different levels: 1) at the "global" level, where the influence can be characterized by the global statistics (i.e., noise power spectrum) of the background in relation to the signal associated with the nodule, and 2) at the "local" level, where the background pattern immediately surrounding the nodule becomes the focus. At the "global" level, the detectability of a nodule is determined by the degree of its distinctiveness from "false positives" created by the overall noise characteristics of the background. At this level, the detection is independent of the nodule location. Many investigators have used the global approach to model the detection of lesions in medical images and it has proved valid for some detection tasks.[17,10,18–20] However, there have been indications that slight changes in the location of a nodule placed upon a lung anatomical background affect its detection dramatically,[21] suggesting that "local" interference plays an important role.

This study is designed to specifically substantiate the influence of the "local" background pattern on the detectability of lung nodules through an observer performance experiment. The study aims at measuring the average detectability of subtle lung nodules against the lung anatomical backgrounds of digital chest radiographs and variation in detectability due to change in the location of the nodule with respect to the background.

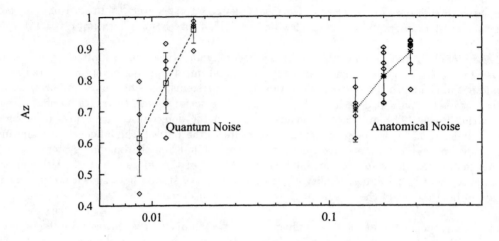

Figure 1: *The average performance index, A_z, as a function of the peak contrast-diameter product (CD) of the nodules superimposed upon quantum noise and anatomical noise images. The individual observer data are also plotted ($\diamond$). The error-bars show the $\pm 2SE$ (SE = standard error) intervals calculated using Swets method.*

2   METHODOLOGY

2.1   Preparation of the Lung Background Images

Six normal PA chest radiographs from our routine clinical operation were selected for use in this study. Radiographs were acquired with a Computed Radiography (CR) upright chest unit (FCR-9501-HQ, Fuji Medical Systems, USA), using 35×43 cm^2 standard-resolution imaging plates (ST-Va, Fuji Medical Systems), and a moving 12:1 anti-scatter grid (Gilardoni). In order to verify that the images are normal, the radiology reports were reviewed and the images examined to assure that the patients have been diagnosed to be free from any acute pulmonary abnormality. For all the chest exposures, a 115 kVp x-ray beam from a high-frequency x-ray generator (1050 HF, Acoma) was used and the exposure was photo-timed using an automatic exposure control (AEC) calibrated to operate the CR system as a 200-speed-equivalent system (22.7 mR entrance exposure for a typical 22-cm-thick patient). The CR Sensitivity (S) values of the radiographs ranged from 196 to 348 (271 mean).

For each chest radiograph, the CR reader creates a 4k (3520 $\times$ 4280), 10-bit, log-scale digital image file[22,23] that is stored on a connected workstation (HIC-654, Fuji Medical Systems). The raw 4k image data of the six selected radiographs were transferred as 2k data (1760 $\times$ 2140) from the CR workstation to a research workstation (Sparc 2, Sun) through a SCSI connection (DASM-FDLR, Analogics, Inc.). Earlier studies have shown that the image quality characteristics of the 4k-reduced 2k images of FCR-9501-HQ system are comparable to those of standard 2k images of this system.[24] From the acquired chest images, six 8×8 cm image blocks (400 $\times$ 400 array) were extracted at random positions within the lung regions of the radiographs.

2.2 Insertion of Simulated Nodules

Simulated nodules emulating the radiographic characteristics of tissue-equivalent lesions were numerically superimposed at the central area of the six lung images. The superpositioning was performed by subtracting the nodule contrast profiles from the log-signal data of the images. The subtraction was done by transforming the desired contrast (dE/E) into the log-signal units associated with the latitude (L) of the acquired CR image. The simulated nodules were circular with subject-contrast profiles according to a mathematical function deduced from a database of real lung nodules[25] as

$$c(r) = C \left(\frac{4.0}{D^4} r^4 - \frac{4.2}{D^2} r^2 + 1 \right) \qquad -0.6D \leq r \leq 0.6D \qquad (1)$$

where $c(r)$ is the contrast (dE/E) as a function of radial distance, r, C is the peak contrast of the nodule, and D is the diameter of the nodule at the image plane specified as the full-width-at-fifth-maximum of the profile. In an earlier study we have shown the radiographic appearance of such simulated nodules is indistinguishable from real lesions.[21]

A peak contrast-diameter ratio for the nodules was selected so that it would correspond to those expected from spherical, uniform, tissue-equivalent lesions within the lung.[25] Five different sizes of simulated nodules were used in the study with contrast-diameter products resulting in a range of average detectability from $A_z \sim 0.6$ to $A_z \sim 0.95$, as determined in a previous study (Figure 1).[16] Table 1 tabulates the characteristics of the simulated nodules that were used in the study.

For each of the six lung images, a set of thirty-one processed images was produced, six containing no nodule, and the remaining 25 containing single nodules of five different sizes placed at five different locations, one at the center and four at 6 mm distance from the center. Figure 2 shows the locations of the nodules in the six lung images used in the study. The location of the nodules among images was varied as a precaution to avoid any visual indication of the locations to the observers, while allowing different local background patterns to overlay the nodules. This scheme generates a total of 150 lung images with superimposed simulated nodules and 36 controls for a total of 186 images to be used in the observer experiment.

After insertion of the nodules, the log-signal values of each image were transformed to film density values using a density versus log-signal transformation developed at HFHS.[16] This operation constructs a Hurter and Driffield (HD) characteristic curve using two Gaussian gradient functions of contrast versus log-signal. For each Gaussian component, the maximum contrast, standard deviation, and mean are specified. The cumulative integral of the Gaussian components is then calculated as the HD curve. For this study, a HD curve was constructed and used similar to that of a conventional screen-film system for chest radiography (Kodak, Ortho-C/Lanex). For each image, prior to insertion of the nodules, the average pixel value from a 128×128 central block was obtained

Table 1: *The peak subject contrast, C, full-width-at-fifth-maximum diameter, D, contrast-diameter products (CD), and the predicted A_z of the simulated nodules used in the observer performance experiment. The nodule dimensions were specified at the image plane. The C/D ratio of these nodules was similar to that expected from spherical, tissue-equivalent lesions in the lung, assuming a scatter-to-primary ratio of 0.68.*

Predicted A_z	0.6	0.7	0.8	0.9	>0.9
CD (mm)	0.1	0.14	0.20	0.28	0.4
C (dE/E)	0.031	0.037	0.044	0.052	0.063
D (mm)	3.19	3.78	4.52	5.35	6.39

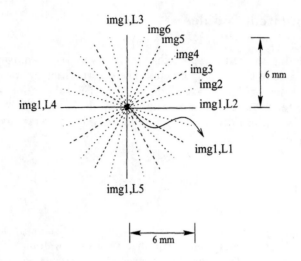

Figure 2: *Five locations of the simulated nodules superimposed at the center of the lung images. The nodule locations (L1 to L5) were sequentially rotated by 15° for different images used in the study (img1 to img6).*

and used as the mean value for the higher-contrast Gaussian component. This ensured the average contrast and optical density at the center of all images, where the nodules were inserted, were constant. The images were padded with 2.6 cm horizontal and 4.1 cm vertical margins of 1.8 constant optical density to create visual glare characteristics during the reading sessions similar to those present in reading a regular chest radiograph. The total of 186 images were then randomized using a random number generator, and printed six-on-one on 31 sheets of film using a laser printer (Kodak, model XLP). The printer was calibrated and its linearity verified between film-densities of 0.1 and 3.0 prior to printing the images. Figure 3 shows an example of a printed film.

2.3 Observer Performance Experiments

Fourteen experienced radiologists participated in the study. Each observer independently read the images in three separate sessions. The sessions were scheduled at least one day apart. At the beginning of each reading session, the observer protocol was explained. The observers were told that there might be a nodule 3 to 6 mm in diameter within 1/2 inch central region of each image. The observer was to discern whether or not a nodule is present in each image, and to indicate his/her confidence level using a five-point grading scale (Table 2). The *a priori* knowledge of the nodules location was expected to result in higher detection rates than those observed in clinical practice. However, this methodology was implemented since the goal of the study was to examine the detection of the nodules when the approximate location was exactly known.

Before each reading session, the observer viewed two graded example films, each containing six images of a lung background with six superimposed simulated nodules of increasing CD values. This was followed by reading two practice films. The observer was subsequently provided with the expected answers so he/she would be able to assess the visibility level of the nodules and adjust his/her grading. All the readings were done on the same viewbox under optimum environmental surroundings. Different observers read the images in different orders to average out any possible memory effect. No time constraints were imposed on the observers but they were constrained to a minimum viewing distance of 30 cm. The average reading time for each session (10-11 films, 60-66 images) was 15 minutes.

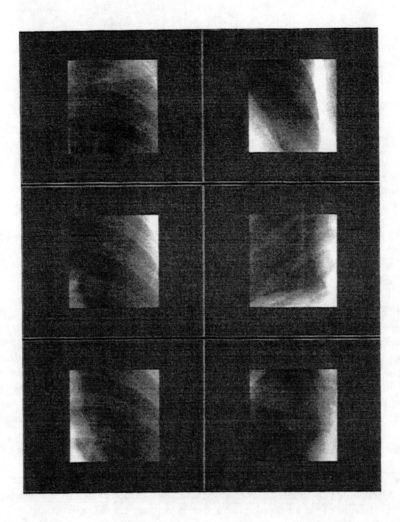

Figure 3: *An example of a printed film with the six images used in the study. Nodules of various CD are superimposed at the center of the images.*

The observer data were analyzed to determine the detectability of the nodules for each image averaged over all observers as a function of the nodule CD product. The scores were also analyzed with respect to the locations of the nodules to determine the variation in detectability as the nodule location is varied against an anatomical background. This variation was also compared to that due to change in the nodule size to evaluate the magnitude of the interference of the local background with the detection task.

3 RESULTS

The results of this study are based on the summary data shown in Figure 4. For reference, the average and standard deviation of the scores corresponding to the control images (no nodules) are shown at CD = 0.06 mm. In general, there is a gradual increase in the average score as a function of the CD of the nodule. Noteworthy are images No. 1 and 6. In image No. 1 (Figure 3, upper-left), the presence of an opacity at the center of the image

Table 2: *Grading scale to score the detected nodules.*

Grade	Criteria
-2	most likely not present
-1	probably not present
0	equivocal
+1	probably present
+2	most likely present

led to a false-positive score for most of the readings. Consequently, the average scores for the low-CD nodules were shifted to higher values. In image No. 6 (Figure 3, lower-right), a calcified costal cartilage was present at the center of the image which greatly obscured the simulated nodules. The complexities of the backgrounds in images No. 4 and 5 also shows an obvious effect on the shape of the observer response.

The error-bars in Figure 4 show ± 1 standard deviation of the average score due to variation in the position of the nodules. There was a general correlation between the scores for nodules of different CD products with respect to their location except the first 3 CD nodules in image No. 1 (due to the false-positive), the first 2 CD nodules in image No. 4 (due to complexity of the background), and the smallest CD nodule in image 6 (due to the obstruction of the calcified cartilage). The average scores for these 6 cases were also comparable to those of the controls, which confirms that location was not an influence in those cases. Comparing the scores for the images containing nodules with the range of the scores for the control images, it is also apparent that for the smallest nodules (CD = 0.1 mm), the deviation of the scores as a function of location cannot be substantiated.

The overall results are summarized in Figure 5 for all observers and all images. In order to generate this figure, the scores for image No. 1, images with smallest size nodules (CD = 0.1), and cases with no locational correlation (image No. 4, CD = 0.14 mm, and image No. 6, CD = 0.14 and 0.2 mm) were eliminated. The error-bars again show ± 1 standard deviation of the average score due to change in the location of the nodules. In order to be able to appreciate the influence of the nodule location, one may compare this deviation to that due to the nodule size: changes in a nodule's position cause a variation in score which is equivalent to that caused by changing the nodule's CD product by a factor of 4.45. This figure was determined using the slope of a linear regression fit to the average score-log(CD) relationship of Figure 5, and ± 1 average standard deviation of the data. Although an ROC analysis has not been performed on these results, by making a comparison to the previous results shown in Figure 1, this change can be seen to correspond to about 0.28 change in the area under the ROC curve (A_z).

4 DISCUSSION

In the early 1970's, Kundel and Revesz adapted Engel's concept of conspicuity[26,27] to measure the contribution of the "local" background lung structure in the detection of lung nodules.[15] Their measurement of conspicuity showed good agreement with the results of early observer studies.[15,28-30] However, some later studies indicated that this measure maybe inadequate to fully quantify the influence of the background structure.[31-33] Others have studied the effects of background variability in computed tomography,[34] dental radiography,[10] and nephrography of rabbits.[17] These approaches consider average, or "global," characteristics of object variability (e.g., the root-mean-square or the variance of the fluctuations) and do not take into account the spatial characteristics of the background structure or the possible local correlation of the background noise with the signal, a situation that is commonly encountered in detection of lung nodules in chest radiographs.

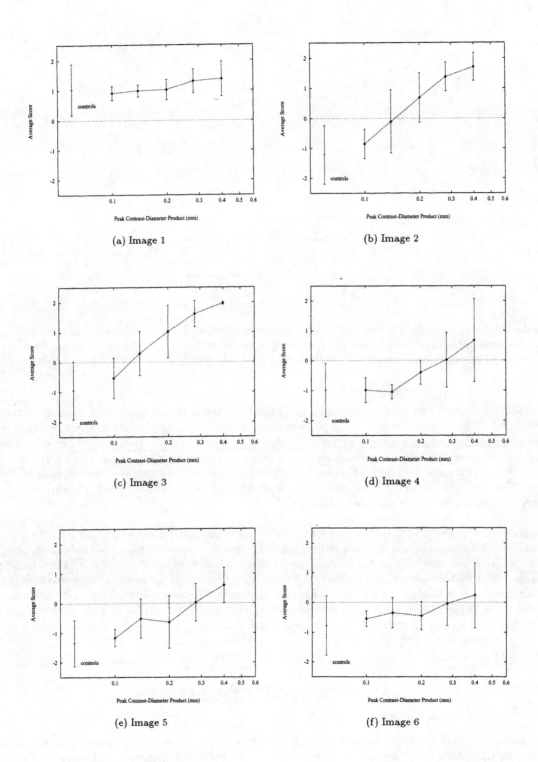

Figure 4: *The average score as a function of nodule CD product for the six images used in the study. The error-bars show ± 1 standard deviation of the average score as the nodule location was varied in the images. For reference, the average and standard deviation of the scores corresponding to the control images (no nodules) are shown at CD = 0.06 mm.*

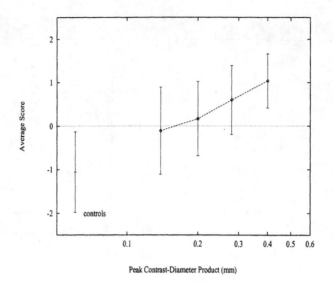

Figure 5: *The average score as a function of nodule CD product averaged over images (image No. 1 and nodules with CD = 0.1 mm eliminated). The error-bars show ± 1 standard deviation of change observed as the nodule location was varied in the images. The single data point at CD = 0.06 corresponds to the control images containing no nodules.*

The spatial characteristics of anatomical noise have been taken into account in a number of recent studies.[19,35,36,18] Some of these studies attempt to determine the accuracy of mathematical observer models to represent the performance of human observers. In order to keep the mathematical model tractable, these studies use synthesized images in which given signals are superimposed upon simple non-uniform background patterns. These simulations are not presently advanced enough to be applied to the complex backgrounds of chest radiographs. However, more recent studies have begun to develop some elegant approaches toward quantifying the influence of anatomical backgrounds in real images.[11,37–39]

In this work we used actual clinical images to quantify the influence of the local background pattern on the detection of subtle lung nodules in chest radiographs. The preliminary results of the study show that, keeping the contrast and diameter of a subtle nodule (3.8-6.4 mm in diameter) the same, changing the location of the nodule in a chest radiograph can greatly vary its detectability (an A_z change of about 0.28 assuming $\pm 1\sigma$). This variation is equivalent to that caused by changing the contrast-diameter product of a nodule at a fixed location by a factor of 4.45 (for spherical tissue-equivalent nodules, changing the diameter of a nodule by a factor of 2.1). Further research focusing on reducing the influence of the local background on the detection of lung nodules in chest radiographs is warranted.

5   ACKNOWLEDGMENTS

The participation of the following individuals in the observer performance experiment is greatly appreciated: G. Beute, R. Chesbrough, B. Craig, D. Eurman, W. Eyler, P. Feczko, N. Gregory, R. Halpert, J. Maltzman, M. Pantelic, J. Pearlberg, D. Spizarny, K. Stuck, and D. Wang. Thanks are also due to Mary Ann Kozlowski for assisting with the reading sessions. This work was supported by a Small Project Grant from the Henry Ford Health Sciences Center.

6 REFERENCES

[1] J.R. Muhm, W.E. Miller, R.S. Fontana, D.R. Sanderson, and M.A. Uhlenhopp. Lung cancer detected during a screening program using four-month chest radiographs. *Radiology*, 148:561–565, 1983.

[2] C.V. Zwirewich, S. Vedal, R.R. Miller, and N.L. Muller. Solitary pulmonary nodule: High-resolution CT and radiologic-pathologic correlation. *Radiology*, 179:469–476, 1991.

[3] ACS. *Cancer Facts and Figures-1993*. American Cancer Society, Atlanta, GA, 1993.

[4] C.F. Mountain. Value of the new TNM staging system for lung cancer. *Cancer*, 96:47s–49s, 1989.

[5] L.W. Guiss and P. Kuenstler. A retrospective view of survey photofluorocarbons of persons with lung cancer. *Cancer*, 13:91–95, 1960.

[6] F.P. Stitik. Chest radiology. In Miller, editor, *Screening for Cancer*, pages 163–191. Academic Press, 1985.

[7] R.T. Heelan, B.J. Flehinger, M.R. Melamed, M.B. Zaman, and W.B. Perchick. Non-small-cell lung cancer: results of the New York screening program. *Radiology*, 151:289–293, 1984.

[8] A. Rose. The sensitivity performance of the human eye on an absolute scale. *Journal of the Optical Society of America*, 38:196–208, 1948.

[9] A.E. Burgess, R.F. Wagner, and R.J. Jennings. Human signal detection performance for noisy medical images. IEEE Computer Society International Workshop on Medical Imaging, pages 99–105, 1982.

[10] U.E. Ruttimann and R.L. Webber. A simple model combining quantum noise and anatomical variation in radiographs. *Medical Physics*, 11:50–60, 1984.

[11] H.H. Barrett. Objective assessment of image quality: Effects of quantum noise and object variability. *Journal of Optical Society of America A*, 7:1266–1278, 1990.

[12] R.G. Greening and E.P. Pendergrass. Postmortem roentgenography with particular emphasis upon the lung. *Radiology*, 62:720–724, 1954.

[13] R.M. Boynton and W.R. Bush. Recognition of forms against a complex background. *Journal of Optical Society of America*, 46:758–764, 1956.

[14] M.J. Smith. *Error and Variation in Diagnostic Radiology*. Charles C. Thomas, Springfield, IL, 1967.

[15] G. Revesz, H.L. Kundel, and M.A. Graber. The influence of structured noise on the detection of radiologic abnormalities. *Investigative Radiology*, 9:479–486, 1974.

[16] E. Samei. *The Performance of Digital X-ray Imaging Systems in Detection of Subtle Lung Nodules*. Doctoral Dissertation, The University of Michigan, Ann Arbor, MI, 1997.

[17] G.W. Seeley, H Roehrig, and B.J. Hillman. A computerized method for measurement of conspicuity: Comparison of film and digital nephrograms. *Investigative Radiology*, 19:583–586, 1984.

[18] A.E. Burgess. Statistically defined backgrounds: Performance of a modified nonprewhitening observer model. *Journal of Optical Society of America A*, 11:1237–1242, 1994.

[19] J.P. Rolland and H.H. Barrett. Effect of random background inhomogeneity on observer detection performance. *Journal of Optical Society of America A*, 9:649–658, 1992.

[20] P.F. Judy, R.G. Swensson, and M. Szulc. Lesion detection and signal-to-noise ratio in CT images. *Medical Physics*, 8:13–23, 1981.

[21] E. Samei, M.J. Flynn, G.H. Beute, and E. Peterson. Comparison of observer performance for real and simulated nodules in chest radiography. volume 2712 of *SPIE Medical Imaging*, pages 60–70, 1996.

[22] E. Samei and M.J. Flynn. Physical measures of image quality in photostimulable phosphor radiographic systems. volume 3032 of *SPIE Medical Imaging*, pages 328–338, 1997.

[23] D.M. Tucker and P.S. Rezentes. The relationship between pixel value and beam quality in photostimulable phosphor imaging. *Medical Physics*, 24:887–893, 1997.

[24] M.J. Flynn, E. Samei, and D.A. Riemann. Experimental comparison of noise and resolution for 2k and 4k storage phosphor chest radiography systems. *Radiology*, 201(P):328, 1996.

[25] E. Samei, M.J. Flynn, and W.R. Eyler. Simulation of subtle lung nodules in projection chest radiography. *Radiology*, 202:117–124, 1997.

[26] F.L. Engel. Visual conspicuity, directed attention and retinal locus. *Vision Research*, 11:563–576, 1971.

[27] F.L. Engel. Visual conspicuity and selective background interference in eccentric vision. *Vision Research*, 14:459–471, 1974.

[28] G. Revesz and H.L. Kundel. Psychophysical studies of detection errors in chest radiology. *Radiology*, 123:559–562, 1977.

[29] H.L. Kundel and G. Revesz. Lesion conspicuity, structured noise, and film reader error. *AJR*, 126:1233–1238, 1976.

[30] H.L. Kundel, G. Revesz, and L. Toto. Contrast gradient and the detection of lung nodules. *Investigative Radiology*, 14:18–22, 1979.

[31] J.R. Hallberg, C.A. Kelsey, and D. Briscoe. Some effects of method on the measured conspicuity of chest lesions. *Investigative Radiology*, 13:439–443, 1978.

[32] B.G. Brogdon, R.D. Moseley, C.A. Kelsey, and J.R. Hallberg. Perception of simulated lung lesions. *Investigative Radiology*, 13:12–15, 1978.

[33] G. Revesz. Conspicuity and uncertainty in the radiographic detection of lesions. *Radiology*, 154:625–628, 1985.

[34] R.G. Swensson and P.F. Judy. Background area effects on feature detectability in CT and uncorrelated noise. *Radiology*, 192P, 1987.

[35] K.J. Myers, J.P. Rolland, H.H. Barrett, and R.F. Wagner. Aperture optimization for emission imaging: Effect of a spatially varying backgrounds. *Journal of Optical Society of America A*, 7:1279–1293, 1990.

[36] K.J. Myers, H.H. Barrett, M.C. Bergstrom, D.D. Patton, and G.W. Seeley. Effect of noise correlation on detectability of disk signals in medical imaging. *Journal of Optical Society of America A*, 2:1752–1759, 1985.

[37] A.E. Burgess, X. Li, and C.K. Abbey. Visual signal detectability with two components: Anomalous masking effects. *Journal of Optical Society of America A*, 14:2420–2442, 1997.

[38] M.P. Eckstein, C.K. Abbey, and J.S. Whiting. Human versus model observer performance in anatomical backgrounds. volume 3340 of *SPIE Medical Imaging*, 1998.

[39] C.K. Abbey, H.H. Barrett, and M.P. Eckstein. Stabilized estimates of hotelling-observer detection in patient-structured noise. volume 3340 of *SPIE Medical Imaging*, 1998.

Prewhitening revisited

Arthur E. Burgess

Radiology Dept., Brigham and Women's Hospital
Harvard Medical School, 75 Francis St., Boston, MA 02115

ABSTRACT

Previous experiments using highpass noise have either suggested that humans cannot compensate for (pre-whiten) anti-correlated noise in images [Myers et al., 1985] or were inconclusive [Burgess, Wagner and Jennings (1982), Burgess (1984)]. These results may have been misleading because of the use of a single noise component. For large exponents of f^n, image noise within the bandwidth of the signal becomes very low and model observers require very little signal amplitude for detection. This situation does not correspond to CT or SPECT imaging cases where patient structure with a lowpass spectrum is also present and limits detection accuracy. In addition, humans have two forms of internal noise that limit detection and this may have been the source of poor human performance. So, in this work, experiments were done with two noise components - one broadband to ensure that task performance was always limited by external noise. The experiments were designed to be more precise test of compensation for (pre-whitening of) anti-correlated noise and to provide a more sensitive test of existing observer models. In all cases, separate experiments were done to estimate observer internal noise. The new results show a marked asymmetry between lowpass and highpass noise effects and are consistent with the view that internal noise is the cause of poor highpass noise performance.

1. INTRODUCTION

Medical images are invariably degraded by noise - which limits observer ability to detect, discriminate and identify lesions. Human observer models can be divided into two broad classes. One is based on the ideal prewhitening (PW) matched filter strategy suggested by North (1943) for radar applications and by Harris (1964) for image discrimination tasks. The other class is based on sub-optimal nonprewhitening (NPW) matched filters (Wagner and Weaver, 1972). In both model classes, the observer is assumed to use the signal as a template for cross-correlation, which is the optimum method if the noise is uncorrelated. However, if the noise is correlated then an additional, prewhitening, procedure is needed for optimum performance. The NPW model assumes that the observer is unable to modify the template to prewhiten correlated noise. The PW and NPW models are identical for white noise and uniform backgrounds.

PW models: The prewhitening observer performs the detection task by cross-correlation of the image data and a template centered at the expected signal locations. The template spatial function is calculated using the exactly known signal function and the covariance matrix of the data, and serves to simultaneously compensate for noise correlations (pre-whiten) and detect the signal. See Myers et al. (1990) for a complete theoretical description. Assuming circular symmetry, the signal has amplitude spectrum, S(f), as a function of radial frequency and the noise has the power spectrum, N(f). The PW observer performance is described by the detectability index, d', with equations of the form:

$$(d')^2 = \int \frac{S^2(f)}{N^2(f)} f df$$

Equation (1)

FH models. Barrett and coworkers [Barrett et al. (1993)] have used a related model, called the Hotelling observer or, alternatively, the Fisher-Hotelling (FH) linear discriminant function model. This model is useful for tasks where the ideal observer performance calculation is non-linear and can not be calculated. If all noise and backgrounds have Gaussian probability distributions, the FH model is also equivalent to the Bayesian ideal prewhitening (PW) observer model for signal known exactly (SKE) detection and discrimination tasks.

Channels models: The PW model has been modified to include spatial frequency channels selected to be one octave wide, consistent with a large variety of psychophysical bandwidth estimates. Myers and Barrett (1987) and Barrett et al. (1993) used non-overlapping channels Rect function channels. The model was artificial for two reasons. (1) The Rect function channels (chosen for mathematical convenience) are very unlike the overlapping channels suggested by psychophysical and physiological experiments (Graham, 1991). (2) In addition, they used an arbitrary low frequency cut-off, f_0, to remove the DC and lowest frequency noise contributions. More realistic channels models have been used by in a number of publications including Eckstein and Whiting (1996), Burgess et al. (1997A and 1997B).

NPW models: There is a long history to this class of model - which does not compensate for noise correlations. They were used in early image quality models, for example (Wagner and Weaver, 1972). Rolland and Barrett (1992) concluded that it was not a suitable model for human detection in statistically defined backgrounds. This is not surprising because the simplest NPW model has no provision for eliminating random DC (zero spatial frequency) level variations - something that is not a problem for human observers. It should be noted that nearly all models in the conventional spatial vision literature are implicitly NPW models [see Graham (1991) and Nachmias (1993)].

Eye filters in image quality models: This issue has a long history - as discussed in Wagner and Weaver (1972). Schade (1956) used an eye filter model in his characterization of effects of image blur and noise. It has been used in figures of merit measuring image resolution in complex scenes by Rindfleish and Willingham (1966); in prewhitening matched filter-based image quality models by Lawson (1971), Halmshaw (1971) and Goodenough (1972); and in nonprewhitening matched filter models by DeBelder et al. (1971) and many others over the years. For example, Burgess et al. (1981) and Loo et al. (1984) used eye filters explicitly in human observer models. A typical eye filter has the form $E(f) = f^m H(f)$ where the exponent 'm' has a value between 1 and 2. The best value is probably unity (Barten, 1992). The lowpass filter, $H(f)$, is usually either exponential or Gaussian - but other variants exist. The eye filter plays an important role in the NPW model since it has no DC response and very poor response at low frequencies. Other methods have been suggested to eliminate the DC variation problem. Myers and Barrett (1987) set model observer response to zero below an arbitrarily selected frequency in a PW channels model. Tapiovaara and Wagner (1993) used non-DC response in an NPW model.

Internal noise in observer models. This topic also has a long history - dating back more than a century as summarized by Burgess and Colborne (1988). They also showed, for one component white noise experiments, that observer variability explained most of the drop in human efficiency. They were the first to demonstrate that the major effect appears to be intrinsic observer noise induced by image noise. They included this induced internal noise in observer models by setting the effective image noise spectral density, $N_{eff} = (1+\beta)N_0$, dependent on the actual image noise spectral density, N_0. They estimated the value of β to be about 0.6 from a large number of experiments. This β value sets an upper limit of about 60% for human observer efficiency for compact, aperiodic signal detection where total human efficiency is found to be about 50%. The generic NPW observer model equation with an eye filter and internal noise has the form

$$(d')^2 = \frac{\left[\int |S(f)|^2 |E(f)|^2 \, fdf \right]^2}{\int (1+\beta) N(f)|S(f)|^2 |E(f)|^4 \, fdf + \int N_i(f) fdf} \qquad \text{Equation (2)}$$

Experimental investigations: Until recently, most medical imaging research on human visual performance modeling concentrated on detection, discrimination and identification of simple signals in either white noise or CT noise on uniform backgrounds. That research was designed to investigate a number of fundamental issues related to human capabilities. The uniform background case is not representative of clinical images; which have non-uniform backgrounds that vary from patient to patient. Myers et al. (1990) did a theoretical evaluation of signal detection in combinations of white noise and statistically defined (lumpy) backgrounds with correlation distances large compared to signal size. The purpose of this work was to develop an understanding of nuclear medicine collimator design. Rolland and Barrett (1992) measured human observer performance with lumpy backgrounds. Yao (1994) investigated detection with both lumpy backgrounds and high-pass noise. Their human results were consistent with the FH model but not with the NPW model (no eye filter). Burgess (1994) showed that the NPWE model, with an eye filter, did fit the Rolland and Barrett human results. Their results were not precise enough to allow distinction between the FH and NPWE models - which gave equally good fits to all of the data.

Burgess et al. (1997A and 1997B) did several types of more precise observer experiments designed to measure performance over a wide range of background spectral density variation to provide a more sensitive test of realistic observer models. The first experiments by Burgess et al. (1997A) were done using backgrounds of variable RMS contrast and several fixed correlation distances large compared to signal size. The white noise amplitude standard deviation was fixed at 20 gray levels.The second noise component spectral density varied over 3 orders of magnitude. This noise component was produced by filtering Gaussian white noise so the PW matched filter and the FH models were identical. The PW model did not agree completely with the human data since model performance decreased more slowly than human observer results as background spectral densities increased. Burgess et al. were able to show that there is no selection of NPWE model parameters that could fit human observer data. These results suggested that perhaps neither of the two extreme views on prewhitening (or, alternatively, template adjustment) is correct. One interpretation is that humans may be able to partially compensate for spatial correlations in lowpass noise or background. The results could be fitted very well using the PW model with channel strategies that were different from those proposed by Myers and Barrett (1987). One model used both an eye filter and one octave Rect channels down to DC, then performance averaging over channel starting frequency. The other model had overlapping channels followed by decorrelation. The other type of experiment done by Burgess et al. (1997A and 1997B) used several types of power spectra for the second noise component and a range of noise bandwidths. These results were also inconsistent with the NPWE model. Good fits were obtained using prewhitening models, particularly with spatial frequency channels.

Human Prewhitening? Some early experiments [Burgess, Wagner and Jennings (1982), Burgess (1984) and Myers et al. (1985)] were specifically designed to investigate whether humans can compensate for noise correlations (prewhiten). These experiments were analyzed using the basic PW and NPW models. The results of Burgess et al. were not conclusive, mainly because only two different spectra were used, white and ramp noise [spectrum form, $N(f) = N_0 f H^2(f)$ where $H(f)$ is a lowpass filter]. Results for a variety of tasks are shown in Fig.1. The d' ratios are averages for 4 observers calculated using both PW and NPW models without an eye filter. If a model is correct the ratio should equal unity for all tasks. Clearly, neither of the two simple models is correct. Some results were consistent with the non-prewhitening hypothesis while others were not. The work by Myers et al. was much improved because they used a wider range of highpass spectra [form, $N(f) = N_0 f^n H^2(f)$ with $n = 0$ to 4]. Human observer performance was measured for one task - SKE detection of a 2D Gaussian signal (15 pixel diameter) with amplitude selected to give a constant d' of 10 for the PW matched filter observer. Experiments were done using the ROC method and d' was calculated from A_z. Their results are shown in figure 2, together with their NPW model (without an eye filter) observer predictions and subsequent channelized PW observer predictions from Myers and Barrett (1987). Their results appear to be conclusive, the NPW model was a good predictor of human performance and they concluded that we cannot prewhiten. The question as to why we cannot is still open. One view, due to Myers and Barrett (1987) is that visual system channels limit our ability to prewhiten. They showed that the experimental results could also be fitted (see fig. 2) by the ideal observer model when it was modified to include artificial Rect function spatial frequency channels. Another alternative explanation, induced internal noise, will be discussed in this paper. As can be seen in figure 2, the low values of d' at higher exponents that arose form this experimental method did not give data precise enough to allow comparisons with the more detailed observer models used here. Also, their efficiencies for white noise were low (about 15%) compared to the more common 50% for spatially compact disc signals found in many other experiments (Burgess et a., Judy, etc.). Their efficiencies for highpass noise were also low (about 10 - 20 %) compared to the values reported by other such experiments (Burgess et al., Judy, etc.). The differences cannot be due their use of the ROC method because Judy et al. found 50% with ROC. Yao (1994) investigated detection with both lumpy backgrounds and image noise. The image simulation was arranged so that the signal and lumpy background were filtered by an imaging aperture. Then Poisson noise was added. Finally all the simulated image data was filtered by a high-pass filter, $H(F) = f^{n/2}\exp(-n\beta f^2)$. Her results were consistent with the channelized FH model using Myers and Barrett channels. She did not test other observer models

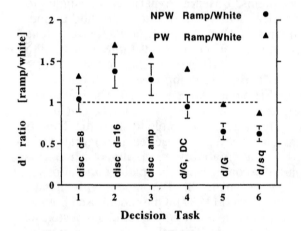

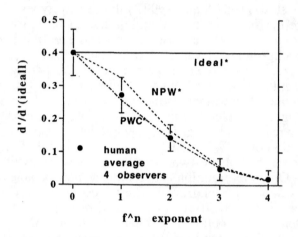

Fig. 1 Ratios of model SNRs (ramp/white) for a fixed human d' (= 2); Burgess (1984) with both detection (1 - 3) and discrimination tasks (4, 5 & 6 with no DC). A correct model would have a ratio equal to 1.0 for all tasks.

Fig. 2. Detectability results for f^n noise from Myers et al. (1985); Myers and Barrett (1987). Scaled models, Ideal, (NPW) nonprewhitening, and (PWC) prewhitening with Rect channels. Reproduced with permission from JOSA.

Two sets of experiments will be presented in this paper. The first set was designed to investigate the effects of both lowpass and highpass noise on signal detection. The second set was designed to study the effects of external noise bandwidth variation on induced internal noise and determine whether this effect could explain poor human performance with highpass noise.

2. METHODS (SPECTRAL EFFECTS)

The experiments on spectral effects were done using the two component noise method to prevent the decision tasks from becoming contrast limited. All filters were chosen to have circular symmetry and noise power spectra can be described using a radial spatial frequency. The two component approach is an extension of the lumpy background method of Rolland and Barrett (1992). Burgess et al. (1997A) used a variety of spectra including Gaussian lowpass and lowpass power law (form $f^{-\beta}$) to simulate a variety of patient structures as well as highpass (form $f^n H^2(f)$] to investigate prewhitening. In the present work, one component (N1) will be broadband noise with a Gaussian amplitude distribution, a lowpass spectrum $N_1(f)$ and variance V_1. The other component (N2) will be filtered Gaussian noise with the spectrum $N_2(f)$ and variance V_2. The variances are constrained by two factors; (1) the 256 gray level dynamic range of the display system and (b) the need to always have some visible image noise so that observer performance was noise-limited. If human performance were contrast-limited (e.g. if the image noise spectral density at any point within the signal spectrum approached zero), model observer threshold amplitudes would be unrealistically small. This requirement sets a lower limit of about 3 gray levels for the broadband N1 noise standard deviation (RMS amplitude) and 8 gray levels was chosen to be clearly in the noise-limited range. The RMS amplitude of the N2 component was chosen in the following way. The NPWE/PW threshold (signal amplitude needed for d' = 2) ratio should be large in order to give good discrimination between observer models. So there should have a large ratio of variances, V_2/V_1. The upper limit of ratio is constrained by the 256 level data range. Fixed RMS amplitudes of 16 and 32 gray levels were chosen as a safe values for the low-pass and highpass filtered noise components respectively. The noise data being send to the display memory was given a mean of 128 gray levels and final images were clipped at zero and 255 to ensure that over-ranging did not occur. Fewer than one pixel in a thousand needed to be clipped.

The lowpass experiments were done using an N2 component with a Gaussian filtered spectrum of the form $N_2(f) = N_{20} \exp(-4\pi^2 s^2 f^2)$, where s is the spatial standard deviation (correlation distance in pixels) and f is the radial spatial frequency in cycles per pixel (the frequency range for an image is 0.0 to 0.5). Examples of these power spectra are shown in figure 3A. The value of s for our experiments was varied over a wide range (zero to 11 pixels) while N_{20} was always selected to give a fixed background amplitude standard deviation (RMS contrast) of 16 gray levels. This power spectrum gave a lumpy-looking background and was designed to mimic some aspects of lung structure in radiographs.

The highpass experiments were done using an N2 component with a spectrum of the form $N_0 f^n H(f)^2$ where $H(f)$ is a low-pass Gaussian filter (s=1) and RMS amplitude of 32 gray levels. Six values of the exponent 'n' were used. Examples of these power spectra are shown in figure 3B. One small difference in experimental design from that of Myers et al. (1985) is the manner of highpass filter selection. They used several functions to simulate filtering before and after image reconstruction from projections. These filters were selected to keep the noise spectrum peak at a constant value (0.108 cycles/mm). The highpass spectra used in this experiment were allowed to have peaks at increasingly high frequencies to more rapidly reduce the amount of N2 component noise within the signal bandwidth as the exponent, n, increased.

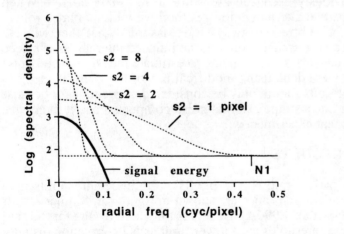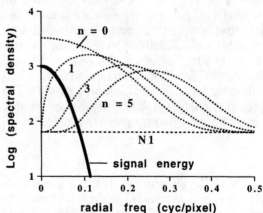

Figure 3. Examples of two component power spectra used in these experiments. Each has a broadband component, N1, with RMS contrast of 8 gray levels. (A) shows lowpass spectra, with various N2 Gaussian filter correlation distances and fixed RMS contrast of 16 levels. (B) shows highpass spectra with N2 various f^n exponents and fixed RMS contrast of 32 levels.

Signals: A variety of tasks were done with two kinds of signals, 2D Gaussian and 2D nodule - but only the nodule signal results will be shown here. The designer nodule (Burgess et al., 1997A), has the radial equation $a(\rho) = \text{Rect}(2\rho)(1-\rho^2)^n$, where ρ is a normalized radius (r/R) in pixels and the exponent, n, is real and non-negative. This generalized nodule function also has a convenient analytic Hankel transform.

Human decision trials. Four trained observers took part in these experiments - three were naive as to the purpose of the experiments. Before experimental data collection began, they did 512 practice trials for each experimental condition (task and noise spectrum combination) selected randomly. During experimental data collection, 768 trials were used for each condition (again randomly selected), giving a coefficient of variation of 7% on estimates of d'. Signal amplitudes for the main trials were chosen to give d' results in the vicinity of 2 (based on practice trial results). The experiments were done using a Tektronix 634 monitor driven by video signals from a Peritek VCU-Q display board in a DEC VAX-4000 host computer. Observations were done using the 2 alternative forced choice (2AFC) method with exactly known signals (SKE). Each block of 256 trials took about 7 minutes on average. Three amplitudes were used for each signal, varied randomly from trial to trial. Observer performance for a given experimental condition was evaluated by determining the percentage of correct responses for each signal amplitude, calculating the corresponding value of the detectability index d', normalizing by the signal to noise ratio (SNR) for that amplitude and averaging over the three amplitudes. Results were then converted to determine the SNR and signal amplitude required for a d' of 2, where coefficients of variation due to sampling error are minimum. In order to allow comparison of human and model results, amplitude threshold predictions for each model were scaled by a constant multiplicative value. The scaling factor was selected to fit human results in the parameter range (white noise end of the scale) where there is essentially no difference in model predictions except for an additional reduction in NPWE statistical efficiency due to the presence of the eye filter.

Internal noise estimates. These experiments were also done using the two component noise method. Two approaches were used to estimate human observer variability and calculate the corresponding internal noise contributions. One is the 2 pass technique where an observer is given the same blocks of image trials in two separate occasions several weeks apart. A completely mechanical and consistent observer would make the same decisions on both passes of the data set. Human observers show variability. Human observer induced internal noise scaling factors, β_1 and β_2, for each of the two external noise components is estimated from the probability of decision agreement for a given trial versus probability of correct 2AFC decision. The other is the twin/different noise field technique. The term "*twin noise*" (suggested by Watson, 1997) is used here to replace the previously used and awkward term "*same noise*". When identical (twin) N2 components are present in the two alternative images then N2 will not play a role in model observer performance because it will be subtracted away. It is assumed that the twin N2 components will contribute to reduction in human performance through the induced internal noise effect. Appropriate substitutions in the observer model equations can be made to estimate the N2 induced noise scaling factor, β_2. The estimates presented here were done using modifications of the analysis methods described by Burgess and Colborne (1988). The results should only be considered as preliminary because the previous analysis methods were designed for one a single external noise component and it likely that they must be modified for these two noise component experiments.

3. RESULTS

Lowpass N2. The results for nodule signal (n=1.5, radius = 4 pixels) amplitude thresholds as a function of the lowpass N2 noise component correlation distance are shown in figure 4A. Similar results were obtained for the 2D Gaussian signal (Burgess et al., 1997A). Observer threshold results for the case of only N1 component noise are also shown - these thresholds set a lower limit as N2 correlation distance increases. There was very little difference in individual observer results and these were consistent with sampling variability. The results show a marked increase in threshold for noise correlation distances close to the signal size. It can be seen that the NPWE model does not agree human results for larger correlation distances. The most important observations about the results are the following. (1) The NPWE model gives a very poor fit to human data while both PW models give much better fits. This suggests that we can definitely compensate for (prewhiten) positive noise correlations. (2) The PW, NPWE and PWCavg model predictions are essentially indistinguishable when background correlation distances are small compared to signal size. (3) Largest differences between models occur when correlation distances are larger than signal size. (4) Sensitivity to observer model properties can be highly variable and depends on the situation under study. The NPWE model has some mathematical features that make it desirable to use and it is clear that there is a region of parameter space where it is valid - but it is clear that the model must be used with care.

Highpass N2. The results for nodule signal ($n=1.5$, radius = 8 pixels) amplitude thresholds as a function of the highpass N2 noise component exponent of f^n are shown in figure 4B. Similar results were obtained for the 2D Gaussian signal. The results show a marked decrease in threshold as the exponent increases. Observer threshold results for the case of only N1 component noise are also shown - these thresholds set a lower limit as the exponent increases. It can be seen that none of the models agree with human results for large exponents. The channelized PW model predictions fall between the two extremes of NPW and PW models. This leads one to suspect that the poor human performance for large exponents has nothing to do with visual channels. There is also much more inter-observer variation than in the lowpass N2 case. The data certainly do demonstrate that the anti-correlated N2 component has a marked effect on signal detection even when very little of the noise is within the signal bandwidth. This suggests that the issue is not whether we can or cannot prewhiten but rather that the local image complexity due to rapid reversals of local contrast makes it difficult for us to perform the detection task.

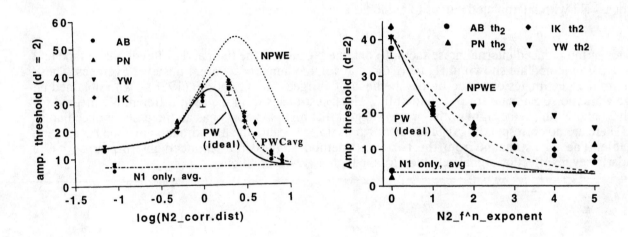

Fig 4. Amplitude thresholds of 4 human observers for nodule signal detection with (A) lowpass and (B) highpass N2 noise. Models are adjusted to fit human data for the white noise conditions ($s=0$ and $n=0$).

Induced internal noise. The results for the twin N2 noise field experiments are shown in figure 5 for the lowpass case (A) and the highpass case (B). The results are averages for 4 observers. The observer averages for the different N2 fields condition are also shown for reference. The curves for the lowpass noise case correspond to PWCavg observer predictions with the induced internal noise factor, β_2, equal to 0.6 - the average value found by Burgess and Colborne (1988). Note for the lowpass case, that twin and different condition amplitude thresholds are virtually identical for large correlation distance. This indicates that relatively smooth lowpass backgrounds play almost no role in threshold elevation for either twin or different conditions. The curves for the highpass N2 case are interpolations through the data points and have no theoretical significance. With highpass N2, there is a small but significant different in thresholds between the twin and different conditions at higher exponents. This indicates that the N2 component continues to play a role in threshold elevation even when there is very little N2 noise within the signal bandwidth.

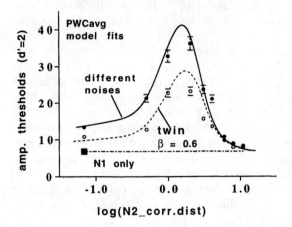 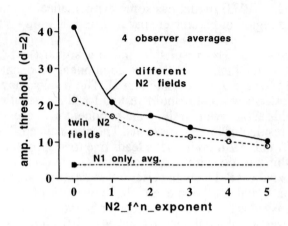

Fig. 5 : Amplitude thresholds for the cases of twin and different N2 noise fields. The data points are averages for 4 observers - (A) lowpass N2 with curves fitted using the PWCavg model with $\beta = 0.6$ and B) highpass N2 with interpolated curves to guide the eye (no theoretical significance).

Estimates of the induced internal noise factor β_2 obtained using (A) the twin and different N2 method and (B) the 2 pass method are shown in figure 6. Once again, the human data are 4 observer averages. These are preliminary estimates obtained by the methods of Burgess and Colborne (1988) - who obtained an average white noise estimate for β_2 found of 0.6. The β_2 estimates from the twin/different N2 method for small N2 bandwidth (to the right of the graph) suggest that highpass noise has an increased induced noise effect. There are no corresponding data for the lowpass noise because the β_2 estimation method became too unreliable. The β_2 estimates from the two-pass method suggest that induced internal noise has a particularly severe effect on signal detection for the highpass N2 condition.

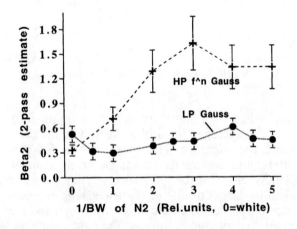 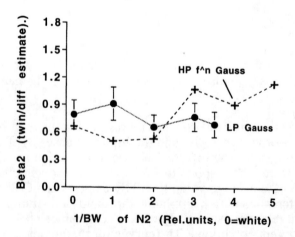

Figure 6. Estimates of the induced internal noise factor, β_2, for the N2 external noise component. The estimates were obtained by two very different ways: (A) the twin/different N2 field method and (B) the two-pass method. These estimates must be considered as very preliminary because they are obtained by analysis methods that were value for single component white noise but may not be valid for two noise components with N2 band-limited noise.

4. DISCUSSION AND CONCLUSIONS

One should first note very carefully that highpass f^n noise is an artificial (experimental) strategy to force large differences between model predictions. This never occurs in practice except for the case of CT and SPECT imaging where the exponent equals one - no medical images have exponents greater than one. The early Burgess et al. and Myers et al. experiments were particularly artificial because there was only ramp noise and no lowpass structure. The two component noise experiments of Yao et al. (1994) were also artificial because the high pass filtering was done on all simulated image components (signal, Poisson noise and lumpy background). This also never occurs in practice. CT and SPECT images always have patient structure (with a lowpass spectrum) to limit detectability. The second major point to note is the marked asymmetry of results between the lowpass and highpass cases - perhaps due to much more induced internal noise when high-pass external noise is present. The lowpass results suggest that we can partially compensate for positive noise correlations. The highpass results suggest that we cannot compensate for negative noise correlations. This should not be surprising since our visual system evolved to deal with a positively correlated world. There are no anti-correlated natural scenes and hence there was no opportunity for us to develop the required compensation techniques.

A number of conclusions can be drawn from our spectral effects results. The obvious one is that detection in the lowpass noise case is most difficult when the signal and the stochastic background (N2) structures have the same size and shape. Signal amplitude thresholds can be raised considerably in this case. A second observation is that prewhitening (PW) models give much better agreement with human results than the non-prewhitening (NPWE) model with an eye filter. For the highpass spectra, none of the models fit the human data. This conclusion is not consistent with the conclusions of Myers et al. (1985 and 1987), who found that both the NPW model (with no eye filter) and the channelized FH model with Rect channels and an arbitrary low frequency cut-off fit their data. My conclusion is also not consistent with the those of Yao (1994) who found that the Myers and Barrett channel model fit her data. There are some important differences in the design of the experiments that may explain the discrepancies. This point needs further investigation. The PW channels averaging model gives excellent agreement with human results for the lowpass N2 case. This supports the conclusions of Barrett et al.(1993) who compared channelized FH model predictions with human performance for a number of other decision tasks. It also supports the conclusions of Burgess et al. (1997A and 1997B) who found excellent agreement, using several channels models. There may be an asymmetry in induced internal noise between the lowpass and highpass noise cases - with much more induced internal noise from high-pass external noise. Some of the preliminary analysis of induced internal noise effects are consistent with this view. However, as was stated several times above, a more appropriate method of analysis must be developed.

In summary. These new conclusions for high pass (f^n) noise are not consistent with the conclusions of Myers et al. (1985), Myers and Barrett (1987) or Yao (1994). These new experiments show that human performance with highpass noise degrades very significantly relative to all models: NPW, PW and Channelized PW cases (which fall between the PW and NPW limits). So the new results cannot be explained by the simple inclusion of channels in a PW model.

5. ACKNOWLEDGMENTS.

I would like to thank Craig Abbey, Philip Judy, Kyle Myers and Bob Wagner for helpful discussions and comments. This research was supported by NIH research grant R01-CA58302.

6. REFERENCES

PGJ Barten, "Physical model for the contrast sensitivity of the human eye",
   SPIE Proc.1666, 57-72 (1992)
HH Barrett, J Yao, JP Rolland and KJ Myers, "Model observers for assessment of image quality".
   Proc. Nat. Acad. Sci. USA 90, 9758-9765 (1993)
AE Burgess, R. F. Wagner and R. J. Jennings: "Human Signal Detection Performance for Noisy Medical Images. Proc. International Workshop on Physics and Engineering in Medical Images."
   IEEE Computer Soc. Cat. No. 82CHl751-7 (1982).

AE Burgess. "Statistical efficiencies of perceptual decisions." SPIE Proc.454, 18-26 (1984)

AE Burgess and B. Colborne, "Visual Signal Detection IV: Observer inconsistency",
J. Opt. Soc. Am. A5, 617-627 (1988)

AE Burgess. "Statistically-defined backgrounds: Performance of a modified nonprewhitening observer model". J. Opt. Soc. Am. A11, 1237-42, (1994).

AE Burgess, "Comparison of Non-prewhitening and Hotelling Observer models".
SPIE Proc. 2436, 1-8 (1995)

AE Burgess, X Li and CK Abbey, "Nodule detection in two component noise: toward patient structure."
SPIE Proc. 3036, 2-13 (1997A)

AE Burgess, X Li, and CK Abbey. "Visual signal detectability with two noise components: anomalous masking effects". J. Opt. Soc. Am. A14, 2420-2442, (1997B)

M DeBelder, R Bollen and R Duvill. "A new approach to the evaluation of radiographic systems."
J. of Photographic Science 19, 126 (1971)

MP Eckstein and JS Whiting, "Visual signal detection in structured backgrounds I. Effect of number of possible spatial locations and signal contrast". J. Opt. Soc. Am. A13, 1777-1787 (1996).

DJ Goodenough. Radiographic applications of signal detection theory.
Ph.D. Thesis, Univ. of Chicago (1972)

N Graham. "Complex channels, early nonlinearities, and normalization in texture segregation".
In Computational Models of Visual Processing, MS Landy and JA Movshon (Edit.),
MIT Press,(1991), pp 273-290

R Halmshaw. "The influence of film granularity on image quality on image detail in radiographs".
J. of Photographic Science 19, 167 (1971)

JL Harris. "Resolving power and decision theory". J. Opt. Soc. Am. 54, 606-622 (1964)

W Lawson. "Electro-optical system evaluation". in Photoelectriconic Imaging Devices Vol. 1, pp375-410 (edit.) LM Biberman and S Nudekman, Plenum Press, New York (1971)

LND Loo, K Doi and CE Metz, "A comparison of physical image quality indices and observer performance in the radiographic detection of nylon beads", Phys. Med. Biol. 29, 837-856 (1984)

KJ Myers, HH Barrett, MC Borgstrom, DD Patton, and GW Seeley, "Effect of noise correlation on detectability of disk signals in medical imaging", J. Opt. Soc. Am. A2, 1752-1759 (1985).

KJ Myers and HH Barrett, "Addition of a channel mechanism to the ideal-observer model",
J. Opt. Soc. Am. A4, 2447-2457 (1987).

KJ Myers, JP Rolland, HH Barrett, and RF Wagner, "Aperture optimization for emission imaging: effect of a spatially varying background", J. Opt. Sci. Am. A7, 1279-1293 (1990).

J Nachmias, "Masked detection of gratings: the standard model revisited",
Vision Res. 33,1359-1365 (1993)

DO North, "Analysis of the factors which determine signal/noise discrimination in radar". RCA Tech. Rep. PTR6C (1943), reprinted in Proc. IRE 51, 1016-1028 (1963)

S Ooue. Progress in Optics VII. 301, Wiley Interscience (1969)

JP Rolland and HH Barrett, "Effect of random background inhomogeneity on observer detection performance", J. Opt. Soc. Am. A9, 649-658 (1992).

MJ Tapiovaara and RF Wagner, "SNR and noise measurement for medical imaging I: A practical approach based on statistical decision theory", Phys. Med. Biol. 38, 71-92 (1993)

RF Wagner and K.E. Weaver, "An assortment of image quality indices for radiographic film-screen combinations-can they be resolved?", SPIE 35, 83-94 (1972)

RF Wagner, DG Brown and MS Pastel, "Application of information theory to the assessment of computed tomography", Medical Physics 6, 83-94 (1979).

RF Wagner and DG Brown: "Unified SNR analysis of medical imaging systems".
Phys. Med. Biol. 30, 489-518 (1985).

AB Watson, suggestion of term "twin "noise during Optical Socierty of America annual meeting (1997)

J Yao and H.H. Barrett, "Predicting human performance by a channelized Hotelling observer model", in Mathematical Methods in Medical Imaging, SPIE Proc. 1768, 161-168 (1992).

J Yao, "Predicting human performance by model observers", Ph. D. dissertation, Univ. of Arizona (1994)

SOME UNLIKELY PROPERTIES OF THE
LIKELIHOOD RATIO AND ITS LOGARITHM

Harrison H. Barrett[*†], Craig K. Abbey[†] and Eric Clarkson[*]
Department of Radiology
Arizona Health Sciences Center
University of Arizona
Tucson, AZ 85724

ABSTRACT

It is well known that the optimum way to perform a signal-detection or discrimination task is to compute the likelihood ratio and compare it to a threshold. Varying the threshold generates the receiver operating characteristic (ROC) curve, and the area under this curve (AUC) is a common figure of merit for task performance. AUC can be converted to a signal-to-noise ratio, often known as d_a, using a well-known formula involving an error function. The ROC curve can also be determined by psychophysical studies for humans performing the same task, and again figures of merit such as AUC and d_a can be derived. Since the likelihood ratio is optimal, however, the d_a values for the human must necessarily be less than those for the ideal observer, and the square of the ratio of d_a(human)/d_a(ideal) is frequently taken as a measure of the perceptual efficiency of the human. The applicability of this efficiency measure is limited, however, since there are very few problems for which we can actually compute d_a or AUC for the ideal observer.

In this paper we examine some basic mathematical properties of the likelihood ratio and its logarithm. We demonstrate that there are strong constraints on the form of the probability density functions for these test statistics. In fact, if one knows, say, the density on the logarithm of the likelihood ratio under the null hypothesis, the densities of both the likelihood and the log-likelihood are fully determined under both hypotheses. Moreover, the characteristic functions and moment-generating functions for the log-likelihood under both hypotheses are specified in terms of a *likelihood-generating function*. From this single function one can obtain all moments of both the likelihood and the log-likelihood under both hypotheses. Moreover, AUC is expressed to an excellent approximation by a single point on the function. We illustrate these mathematical properties by considering the problem of signal detection with uncertain signal location.

1. INTRODUCTION

As noted in an earlier paper in this volume [1], it is often useful to express the results of human perceptual studies in the form of an efficiency, defined as the ratio of the human performance to that of some standard or ideal observer. For signal-detection or classification tasks, performance of both the human and the standard can be expressed in terms of a detectability index d_a derived from an ROC (receiver operating characteristic) curve. The efficiency is then defined as

$$\eta = \frac{d_a^2(\text{human observer})}{d_a^2(\text{standard observer})} .\qquad(1)$$

Most of the research reported in this volume will focus on the numerator in an efficiency expression; we look at the denominator. If the objective of the perceptual study is to quantify human performance relative to the best

---

[*] Also with Optical Sciences Center, Univ. of Arizona.
[†] Also with Program in Applied Mathematics, Univ. of Arizona.

SPIE Vol. 3340 • 0277-786X/98/$10.00

achievable performance, the denominator observer should be an ideal observer. but we have two choices for which ideal observer to use. The earlier paper concentrated on the optimal linear or Hotelling observer; here we discuss the absolute ideal or Bayesian observer.

By definition, the Bayesian ideal observer is one who has full knowledge of the statistical properties of the data and uses it to optimize d_a, Bayes risk or some other measure of performance. It is well known [2, 3] that this oberver computes the likelihood ratio and compares it to a threshold in order to make a decision. Exactly the same decisiion would be obtained by computing the logarithm of the likelihood ratio (or log-likelihood for short) and comparing it to the logarithm of the threshold, so we can equally well define the ideal observer as one that uses the log-likelihood as a test statistic.

The log-likelihood is a random variable, with a value dependent on the random image data used to compute it. To determine an ROC curve for the ideal observer, it is necessary to know the complete statistical properties of the log-likelihood. For a binary hypothesis-testing task such as signal detection, it is necessary to know the probability density functions under both hypotheses. Except for a few simple problems, these densities are not known, and there has been no mechanism for computing the ROC curve. It is for this reason that the Hotelling observer has proven useful: the Hotelling trace can be computed with far less statistical knowledge than is needed for the ideal observer, and hence it has been tractable in a wider range of problems.

Our group has begun to address the issue of determining probability density functions for the likelihood ratio and log-likelihood. A number of surprising and apparently very useful relations have been derived [4]. This paper summarizes those results and illustrates them by discussing a particular problem in signal detection. For more mathematical detail, the reader is referred to [4].

2. MATHEMATICAL BACKGROUND

2.1. Definitions

A digital image consists of a set of M real numbers, often called grey levels or pixel values. We can arrange these values as an $M \times 1$ column vector $\mathbf{g}$, with the mth component being the grey level associated with pixel m. We regard each g_m as a continuous random variable and thus $\mathbf{g}$ as a continuous random vector. In practice, of course, the grey levels are quantized by analog-to-digital conversion or the discrete number of photons contributing to a pixel value, but these effects are not treated here.

An image is related to an object by the action of an imaging system, which can include image-forming elements, image sensors and image-reconstruction algorithms or other computer processing. We do not consider any of these items here in detail. The viewpoint is that the imaging system delivers an image vector $\mathbf{g}$, which we shall use to perform a specific task, and we need only to know the statistical properties of $\mathbf{g}$ to assess the quality of the imaging system.

The task considered here is to decide between two hypotheses, H_0 and H_1. For definiteness we refer to these hypotheses as, respectively, signal-absent and signal-present, but the mathematics applies as well to discrimination between two signals or two object classes. Moreover, we shall allow wide latitude in what is considered to be a signal; the signal is whatever component distinguishes H_1 from H_0. By contrast, in the earlier paper in this volume [1], the signal was nonrandom and known exactly.

We assume that the decision strategy must be nonrandom (a particular image must always lead to the same decision), and it must not allow equivocation (every image must lead to some decision, either signal-present or signal-absent). These conditions imply [2][4] that decision-making can be expressed as a two-step process: first compute a discriminant function $t = \theta(\mathbf{g})$, then compare it to a threshold x. If $t \geq x$, choose hypothesis H_1, otherwise choose H_0.

2.2. The ROC curve and figures of merit

There are four possible outcomes for each individual decision. If the decision is signal-present and it really is present, the decision is a true positive (TP), while a decision of signal-present for an image with no signal is a false positive (FP). The conditional probability of a positive decision, given that the signal is actually present, is called the true-positive fraction (TPF). True negatives (TN) and false negatives (FN) and associated fractions (TNF and FNF) are defined similarly. From basic properties of conditional probabilities, TPF = 1 - FNF and TNF = 1 - FPF, so only two of the four fractions are needed to specify test performance; it is conventional to choose TPF and FPF.

The TPF at threshold x is given by

$$\text{TPF}(x) = Pr(t \geq x | H_1) = \int_x^\infty dt \; pr(t | H_1) \,, \tag{2}$$

where $Pr(t \geq x | H_1)$ is the probability that $t \geq x$ and $pr(t | H_1)$ is the probability density function of the continuous random variable t; both of these quantities are conditional on hypothesis H_1 being true, or signal actually being present. In general, we shall use $Pr(\cdot)$ for probabilities and $pr(\cdot)$ for probability density functions, though other notations will also be introduced for the latter as needed.

The FPF at threshold x is given by

$$\text{FPF}(x) = Pr(t \geq x | H_0) = \int_x^\infty dt \; pr(t | H_0) \,. \tag{3}$$

The threshold x controls the tradeoff between TPF and FPF. Graphically, this tradeoff is portrayed by the ROC curve, which is a plot of $\text{TPF}(x)$ *vs.* $\text{FPF}(x)$.

One possible figure of merit for binary decision problems is the *Bayes risk*, defined by assigning costs and prior probabilities to each of the four possible decision outcomes. The risk value is, however, difficult to interpret. There are no generally accepted rules for defining costs, or even any standard units of measure for them.

Another possible figure of merit, called the Neyman-Pearson criterion, is the TPF at some specified FPF. Computation of this figure of merit requires knowledge of the probability law for the discriminant function under the two hypotheses but not prior probabilities or costs.

Both Bayes risk and TPF at a specified FPF depend not only on the task and the quality of the data but also on the chosen operating point on the ROC curve. The operating point, however, is fairly arbitrary; different users of the image data will assign different costs and priors, and hence use different operating points. For this reason, many workers in signal detection and image quality advocate using the entire ROC curve as the quality metric. A common scalar figure of merit is the area under the ROC curve, denoted AUC. It varies from 0.5 for a worthless system to 1.0 for a system that allows the task to be performed perfectly.

Another figure of merit, which can be defined for any discriminant function t, is the signal-to-noise ratio (SNR), given by

$$\text{SNR}_t^2 \equiv \frac{[\langle t \rangle_1 - \langle t \rangle_0]^2}{\frac{1}{2}\text{var}_1(t) + \frac{1}{2}\text{var}_0(t)} \,, \tag{4}$$

where $\langle t \rangle_j$ denotes the conditional expectation of t given that H_j is true and $\text{var}_j(\cdot)$ denotes the corresponding conditional variance.

If t is normally distributed under both hypotheses, it is well known (and shown in [4]) that SNR_t is related to AUC by

$$\text{AUC} = \frac{1}{2} + \frac{1}{2}\text{erf}\left(\frac{\text{SNR}_t}{2}\right), \tag{5}$$

where $\text{erf}(\cdot)$ is the error function. Thus, in this case there is a simple monotonic relation between AUC and SNR_t, so it doesn't matter which we adopt as a figure of merit.

The quantity d_a mentioned in the introduction is an SNR-like metric (actually referred to as SNR(AUC) in [4]), defined by

$$d_a \equiv 2\,\text{erf}^{-1}(2\,\text{AUC} - 1) \;, \tag{6}$$

where $\text{erf}^{-1}(\cdot)$ is the inverse of the error function. If the test statistic t is normally distributed under both hypotheses, SNR_t and d_a are identical.

The results of psychophysical studies of human-observer performance are almost universally reported in terms of AUC or d_a, so methods of computing these metrics for the ideal observer are needed if we wish to see how nearly the human approximates the ideal.

2.3. Formulas for computing AUC

Ref. [4] gives a detailed discussion of various ways of computing AUC, and hence d_a, depending on what is known about the statistics of the discriminant function. Here we merely summarize some of the main results.

Suppose first that we are given a discriminant function $t = \theta(\mathbf{g})$ and that we know its densities $pr(t|H_0)$ and $pr(t|H_1)$. For notational convenience, we define

$$pr(t|H_j) \equiv p_j(t) \;. \tag{7}$$

The area under the ROC curve is given by

$$\text{AUC} = \int_0^1 \text{TPF}\, d(\text{FPF}) \;, \tag{8}$$

where $\text{TPF}(x)$ and $\text{FPF}(x)$ are given by (2) and (3), respectively. The following equivalent forms follow by straightforward manipulations [4]:

$$\text{AUC} = -\int_{-\infty}^{\infty} dx\, \text{TPF}(x)\, \frac{d}{dx}\text{FPF}(x) \;, \tag{9}$$

$$\text{AUC} = \int_{-\infty}^{\infty} dx\, p_0(x) \int_x^{\infty} dt\, p_1(t) \;. \tag{10}$$

$$\text{AUC} = \frac{1}{2} + \frac{1}{2}\int_{-\infty}^{\infty} dx \int_{-\infty}^{\infty} dt\, p_0(x)\, p_1(t)\, \text{sgn}(t - x) \;. \tag{11}$$

where $\text{sgn}(x) = +1$ if $x > 0$ and -1 if $x < 0$.

The Fourier transform of $\text{sgn}(x)$ is $\mathscr{P}\{1/\pi i\xi\}$, where $\mathscr{P}$ indicates that the singular Fourier integral must be interpreted as a Cauchy principal value. With this relation, (11) becomes

$$\text{AUC} = \frac{1}{2} + \frac{1}{2\pi i}\mathscr{P}\int_{-\infty}^{\infty} \frac{d\xi}{\xi}\, \psi_0(\xi)\psi_1^*(\xi) \;, \tag{12}$$

where $\psi_j(\xi)$ is the characteristic function for t under hypothesis H_j. Specifically,

$$\psi_j(\xi) \equiv \langle \exp(-2\pi i \xi t) \rangle_j = \int_{-\infty}^{\infty} dt \; p_j(t) \exp(-2\pi i \xi t) = \mathscr{F}\{p_j(t)\} \; . \tag{13}$$

The formulas above assume that the densities $p_j(t)$ are known, but we may not have that much information about a test statistic. Suppose now that we know only a few low-order moments of t under the two hypotheses.

The moments can, of course, be related to derivatives of the characteristic function, but it is somewhat more convenient to use the *moment-generating function*, defined by

$$M_j(\beta) = \langle \exp(\beta t) \rangle_j = \int_{-\infty}^{\infty} dt \; p_j(t) \exp(\beta t) = \psi_j\left(\frac{i\beta}{2\pi}\right) \; . \tag{14}$$

If we think of ξ and β as complex variables, the functions $\psi_j(\xi)$ and $M_j(\beta)$ are related by a 90° rotation in the complex plane and a scaling of the argument by 2π.

In terms of moments, AUC is given by

$$AUC = \frac{1}{2} + \frac{1}{2\pi}\mathscr{P}\int_{-\infty}^{\infty} \frac{d\xi}{\xi} \sin\left[2\pi(\overline{t_1} - \overline{t_0})\xi \; - \; \frac{4\pi^3}{3}(\sigma_1^3 S_1 - \sigma_0^3 S_0)\xi^3 + \cdots \right]$$

$$\cdot \exp[-2\pi^2(\sigma_0^2 + \sigma_1^2)\xi^2 + (2\pi^4/3)(\sigma_1^4 K_1 + \sigma_0^4 K_0)\xi^4 + \cdots] \; , \tag{15}$$

where $\overline{t_j}$, σ_j^2, S_j and K_j are, respectively, the mean, variance, skewness and kurtosis of $p_j(t)$. Different definitions of kurtosis appear in the literature, but with the one used here, $K = 0$ for a Gaussian.

3. THE IDEAL OBSERVER

3.1. The test statistic

The test statistic used by the ideal observer is the likelihood ratio, defined by

$$\Lambda(\mathbf{g}) = \frac{q_1(\mathbf{g})}{q_0(\mathbf{g})} \; , \tag{16}$$

where $q_j(\mathbf{g})$ is a shorthand for $pr(\mathbf{g}|H_j)$. Equivalently, the ideal observer can also use the log-likelihood $\lambda(\mathbf{g})$, given by

$$\lambda(\mathbf{g}) = \log[\Lambda(\mathbf{g})] \; . \tag{17}$$

To compute the ideal-observer AUC with the formalism of Sec. 2.3, we need the probability density functions of either Λ or λ under both hypotheses. Equivalently, we can also get AUC from the characteristic functions or moment-generating functions. If these exact specifications prove difficult to get, we can attempt to compute some low-order moments of Λ or λ and relate them approximately to AUC.

With all of these approaches, the ideal observer differs fundamentally from other observers because its discriminant function (whether Λ or λ) already contains all of the relevant statistical information about the task. As we shall see, this fact imposes strong constraints on the forms of the densities, moments or other statistical descriptors.

We shall illustrate these points first in Sec. 3.2 with respect to moments and moment-generating functions, then in Sec. 3.3 for the probability density functions.

3.2. Moments of Λ and λ

The likelihood ratio is a ratio of two densities $q_1(\mathbf{g})$ and $q_0(\mathbf{g})$, and these same two densities are the ones needed to compute moments of Λ under the two hypotheses. It follows at once that the moments under H_0 are related to those under H_1 by

$$\langle \Lambda^{k+1} \rangle_0 = \int_\infty d^M g \; q_0(\mathbf{g}) \left[\frac{q_1(\mathbf{g})}{q_0(\mathbf{g})} \right]^{k+1} = \int_\infty d^M g \; q_1(\mathbf{g}) \left[\frac{q_1(\mathbf{g})}{q_0(\mathbf{g})} \right]^k = \langle \Lambda^k \rangle_1 \; . \tag{18}$$

In particular, the mean of Λ under H_0 is always 1, since

$$\langle \Lambda \rangle_0 = \langle \Lambda^0 \rangle_1 = \int_\infty d^M g \; q_0(\mathbf{g}) \, \frac{q_1(\mathbf{g})}{q_0(\mathbf{g})} = \int_\infty d^M g \; q_1(\mathbf{g}) = 1 \; , \tag{19}$$

and the variance of Λ under H_0 is easily expressed in terms of the mean under H_1:

$$\mathrm{var}_0(\Lambda) = \langle \Lambda^2 \rangle_0 - \langle \Lambda \rangle_0^2 = \langle \Lambda \rangle_1 - 1 \; . \tag{20}$$

Moreover, since $\Lambda = e^\lambda$, we can rewrite (18) as

$$\langle e^{(k+1)\lambda} \rangle_0 = \langle e^{k\lambda} \rangle_1 \; . \tag{21}$$

Since (21) holds for arbitrary (even complex) k, we see that

$$M_0(\beta+1) = M_1(\beta) \; , \tag{22}$$

where $M_j(\beta)$ denotes the moment-generating function for λ under H_j. The corresponding relation for characteristic functions is

$$\psi_0 \left(\xi + \frac{i}{2\pi} \right) = \psi_1(\xi) \; . \tag{23}$$

Notice that $M_0(\beta)$ can be used to generate moments of both λ and Λ under both hypotheses. From (14) with $t = \lambda$, we have

$$\langle \lambda^k \rangle_0 = M_0^{(k)}(0) \; , \tag{24}$$

and with (22),

$$\langle \lambda^k \rangle_1 = M_1^{(k)}(0) = M_0^{(k)}(1) \; . \tag{25}$$

Moments of Λ are found from $M_0(\beta)$ even more simply; moments under H_0 are given by

$$\langle \Lambda^k \rangle_0 = \langle \exp(k\lambda) \rangle_0 = M_0(k) \; , \tag{26}$$

and under H_1 by

$$\langle \Lambda^k \rangle_1 = \langle \exp[(k+1)\lambda] \rangle_0 = M_0(k+1) . \tag{27}$$

3.3. Probability density functions

Since a probability density function is uniquely determined by the corresponding characteristic function, (23) implies that there is a relation between $p_0(\lambda)$ and $p_1(\lambda)$, specifically [4],

$$p_1(\lambda) = e^\lambda p_0(\lambda) . \tag{28}$$

Of course, both $p_0(\lambda)$ and $p_1(\lambda)$ must be properly normalized to unity, so the only functions that can be densities for the log-likelihood under H_0 are ones that remain normalized after multiplication by e^λ, *i.e.*

$$\int_{-\infty}^{\infty} d\lambda \; e^\lambda p_0(\lambda) = 1 . \tag{29}$$

If we know that $p_0(\lambda)$ really is the density for a log-likelihood under H_0, however, (29) is trivially satisfied since it is equivalent to (19).

From (28) we readily find a relation between the densities for Λ under the two hypotheses. Since λ and Λ are related by a monotonic transformation, we can write

$$p_j(\lambda) = \frac{pr(\Lambda|H_j)}{|d\lambda/d\Lambda|} . \tag{30}$$

The Jacobian $|d\lambda/d\Lambda|$ is the same under H_0 and H_1, so (28) becomes

$$pr(\Lambda|H_1) = e^\lambda pr(\Lambda|H_0) = \Lambda pr(\Lambda|H_0) . \tag{31}$$

It is instructive to rewrite this equation as

$$\frac{pr(\Lambda|H_1)}{pr(\Lambda|H_0)} = \Lambda . \tag{32}$$

In this form, the relation was known to Green and Swets [5], who described it as follows: "To paraphrase Gertrude Stein, the likelihood ratio of the likelihood ratio is the likelihood ratio." To paraphrase Green and Swets, the likelihood ratio is a sufficient statistic for deciding between H_0 and H_1. If we were given *any* function of the data, $t(\mathbf{g})$, and we wanted to make an optimal decision based only on $t(\mathbf{g})$ and not on the original $\mathbf{g}$, we would form the likelihood ratio $pr(t(\mathbf{g})|H_1)/pr(t(\mathbf{g})|H_0)$ and compare it to a threshold. In most cases this strategy, though optimal when only $t(\mathbf{g})$ is available, would be inferior to forming the likelihood ratio from the original data, and there would thus be an information loss inherent in using $t(\mathbf{g})$ in place of $\mathbf{g}$. From (32) we see that there is no such information loss if $t(\mathbf{g})$ is the sufficient statistic $\Lambda(\mathbf{g})$.

3.4. Normal log-likelihoods

Much of the literature on the ideal observer has proceeded from the assumption -- implicit or explicit -- that the log-likelihood is normally distributed. It is shown in [4] that there are some very strong restrictions on the statistics of λ if a normal model is to be applicable; we summarize those restrictions here for later reference.

Suppose that λ is normally distributed under H_0 with mean $\overline{\lambda}_0$ and variance $var_0(\lambda)$. One might expect that $\overline{\lambda}_0$ and $var_0(\lambda)$ could be specified independently and that two more independent parameters would be needed to specify the mean and variance under H_1, but this is definitely not the case. The probability density functions for a normal log-likelihood *must* have the form,

$$p_0(\lambda) = \frac{1}{\sqrt{2\pi \text{var}_0(\lambda)}} \exp\left[-\frac{[\lambda + \frac{1}{2}\text{var}_0(\lambda)]^2}{2\text{var}_0(\lambda)}\right] ; \tag{33}$$

$$p_1(\lambda) = \frac{1}{\sqrt{2\pi \text{var}_0(\lambda)}} \exp\left[-\frac{[\lambda - \frac{1}{2}\text{var}_0(\lambda)]^2}{2\text{var}_0(\lambda)}\right] . \tag{34}$$

It is easy to verify that (28) is satisfied. These densities imply that $\text{var}_0(\lambda) = \text{var}_1(\lambda)$ and $\overline{\lambda_1} = -\overline{\lambda_0} = \frac{1}{2}\text{var}_0(\lambda)$. Thus all statistical properties of λ under both hypotheses are determined by the single parameter $\text{var}_0(\lambda)$, starting just from the assumption that λ obeys *some* normal law under H_0.

4. THE LIKELIHOOD-GENERATING FUNCTION

4.1. Definitions and basic properties

In view of (28), both $p_0(\lambda)$ and $p_1(\lambda)$ can be be derived from a single non-negative function $f(\lambda)$ as follows:

$$p_0(\lambda) = e^{-\frac{1}{2}\lambda} f(\lambda) , \qquad p_1(\lambda) = e^{\frac{1}{2}\lambda} f(\lambda) . \tag{35}$$

The characteristic functions and moment-generating functions are determined from $f(\lambda)$ by

$$\psi_0(\xi) = F\left(\xi - \frac{i}{4\pi}\right) , \qquad \psi_1(\xi) = F\left(\xi + \frac{i}{4\pi}\right) , \tag{36}$$

$$M_0(\beta) = F_L(\beta - \tfrac{1}{2}) , \qquad M_1(\beta) = F_L(\beta + \tfrac{1}{2}) , \tag{37}$$

where $F(\xi)$ is the Fourier transform of $f(\lambda)$ and $F_L(\beta)$ is its two-sided Laplace transform,

$$F_L(\beta) = \int_{-\infty}^{\infty} d\lambda \, f(\lambda) \, e^{\beta\lambda} . \tag{38}$$

Normalization of the densities requires that $\psi_j(0) = 0$ and $M_j(0) = 0$, which means that $F(\pm i/4\pi) = 1$ and $F_L(\pm\frac{1}{2}) = 1$. We can enforce these conditions by defining new functions $T(\xi)$ and $G(\beta)$ such that

$$F(\xi) = \exp\left[\left(\xi + \frac{i}{4\pi}\right)\left(\xi - \frac{i}{4\pi}\right)T(\xi)\right] ; \tag{39}$$

$$F_L(\beta) = \exp[(\beta + \tfrac{1}{2})(\beta - \tfrac{1}{2})G(\beta)] . \tag{40}$$

The functions $T(\xi)$ and $G(\beta)$ are related to each other by

$$T(\xi) = -4\pi^2 G(-2\pi i\xi) . \tag{41}$$

If we allow complex arguments, we can derive all statistical properties of the likelihood and log-likelihood from either $T(\xi)$ or $G(\beta)$. We choose to work with $G(\beta)$, which we shall call the likelihood-generating function.

In terms of $G(\beta)$, the characteristic and moment-generating functions for the log-likelihood are given by

$$\psi_0(\xi) = \exp\left[\xi\left(\xi - \frac{i}{2\pi}\right)T\left(\xi - \frac{i}{4\pi}\right)\right] = \exp\left[-4\pi^2\xi\left(\xi - \frac{i}{2\pi}\right)G(-2\pi i\xi - \tfrac{1}{2})\right] ; \tag{42}$$

$$\psi_1(\xi) = \exp\left[\xi\left(\xi + \frac{i}{2\pi}\right)T\left(\xi + \frac{i}{4\pi}\right)\right] = \exp\left[-4\pi^2\xi\left(\xi + \frac{i}{2\pi}\right)G(-2\pi i\xi + \tfrac{1}{2})\right] ; \tag{43}$$

$$M_0(\beta) = \exp[\beta(\beta - 1)G(\beta - \tfrac{1}{2})] ; \tag{44}$$

$$M_1(\beta) = \exp[\beta(\beta + 1)G(\beta + \tfrac{1}{2})] . \tag{45}$$

From these equations we see that the basic requirements $\psi_j(0) = 1$ and $M_j(0) = 1$ are satisfied.

Two equivalent expressions for $G(\beta)$ can be derived from (44) and (45) by changing variables:

$$G(\beta) = \frac{\log M_0(\beta + \tfrac{1}{2})}{(\beta - \tfrac{1}{2})(\beta + \tfrac{1}{2})} = \frac{\log M_1(\beta - \tfrac{1}{2})}{(\beta - \tfrac{1}{2})(\beta + \tfrac{1}{2})} . \tag{46}$$

Moments of the likelihood ratio are easily expressed in terms of $G(\beta)$:

$$\log\langle \Lambda^k \rangle_1 = \log\langle \Lambda^{k+1} \rangle_0 = k(k + 1)G(k + \tfrac{1}{2}) . \tag{47}$$

Furthermore, we can compute SNR_λ if we know $G(\beta)$; the requisite moments are given by

$$\overline{\lambda_0} = -G(-\tfrac{1}{2}) , \qquad \overline{\lambda_1} = G(\tfrac{1}{2}) ; \tag{48}$$

$$\mathrm{var}_0(\lambda) = 2[G(-\tfrac{1}{2}) - G'(-\tfrac{1}{2})] , \qquad \mathrm{var}_1(\lambda) = 2[G(\tfrac{1}{2}) + G'(\tfrac{1}{2})] , \tag{49}$$

where $G'(\beta)$ is the derivative of $G(\beta)$. Hence,

$$\mathrm{SNR}_\lambda^2 = \frac{[G(\tfrac{1}{2}) + G(-\tfrac{1}{2})]^2}{G(\tfrac{1}{2}) + G(-\tfrac{1}{2}) + G'(\tfrac{1}{2}) - G'(-\tfrac{1}{2})} . \tag{50}$$

We see that SNR_λ^2 has the structure X^2/X if the derivative of G is approximately the same at $\tfrac{1}{2}$ and $-\tfrac{1}{2}$. In that case,

$$\mathrm{SNR}_\lambda^2 \simeq \overline{\lambda_1} - \overline{\lambda_0} = G(\tfrac{1}{2}) + G(-\tfrac{1}{2}) \simeq 2G(0) . \tag{51}$$

4.2. Relation of the likelihood-generating function to AUC

The key expression for AUC is (12), which we can rewrite in terms of the likelihood-generating function as

$$\mathrm{AUC} = \frac{1}{2} + \frac{1}{2\pi i}\mathscr{P}\int_{-\infty}^{\infty}\frac{d\xi}{\xi}\exp\left\{-4\pi^2\left(\xi^2 - \frac{i\xi}{2\pi}\right)[G(-2\pi i\xi - \tfrac{1}{2}) + G(2\pi i\xi + \tfrac{1}{2})]\right\} . \tag{52}$$

This integral is dominated by the behavior of $G(\beta)$ near the origin. It is shown in [4] that $G(\beta)$ is analytic in a strip around the origin, so we can expand it in a Taylor series as

$$G(\beta) = \sum_{n=0}^{\infty} \frac{1}{n!} G^{(n)}(0) \, \beta^n \, , \tag{53}$$

where the derivatives $G^{(n)}(0)$ are all real since $G(\beta)$ is real for real β.

As a first approximation, we might assume that the expansion for $G(\beta)$ can be truncated after $n = 1$, so that $G(\beta)$ is approximated by a linear function near the origin. If this approximation is valid, then

$$\text{AUC} \simeq \frac{1}{2} + \frac{1}{2}\text{erf}\left[\frac{1}{2}\sqrt{2G(0)}\right] . \tag{54}$$

AUC is determined solely by $G(0)$ in this approximation.

This calculation extends the range of validity of the error-function formula, (5), with a new SNR defined by $\sqrt{2G(0)}$. As originally derived, (5) held exactly only for Gaussian discriminant functions, which in the case of the ideal observer would mean $G(\beta) = $ constant. Now we see that the formula also holds with non-Gaussian log-likelihoods so long as we can approximate $G(\beta)$ by a linear function near the origin.

Though motivated by the approximation that $G(\beta)$ is linear near the origin, (54) is actually much more general. It is shown in [4] that it is the leading term in an asymptotic expansion for AUC. This expansion becomes arbitrarily precise as $G(0)$ increases; the error must satisfy

$$\left| AUC - \frac{1}{2} + \frac{1}{2}\text{erf}\left[\frac{1}{2}\sqrt{2G(0)}\right] \right| \leq \tfrac{1}{2}\exp[-\tfrac{1}{2}G(0)] . \tag{55}$$

The single value $G(0)$ can also be used to set a lower limit on AUC with no approximations at all. A derivation in [4] shows that

$$AUC \geq 1 - \frac{1}{2}\exp[-\tfrac{1}{2}G(0)] . \tag{56}$$

This inequality provides an exact lower bound for the AUC obtained by an ideal observer, regardless of the probability laws for the data or for the likelihood ratio. As with the approximate formula (54), the bound depends solely on $G(0)$.

5. SIGNAL DETECTION WITH LOCATION UNCERTAINTY

To illustrate the mathematics of the likelihood-generating function, we consider detection of a known signal that can be at one of N non-overlapping locations in white Gaussian noise. This problem was suggested by Barrett, Myers and Wagner [6] as a test case for understanding the effects of signal variability on detection performance, and it was later analyzed in much more detail by Brown, Insana and Tapiovaara [7].

In reference [6] the ideal-observer test statistic was taken fundamentally as the log-likelihood, but it was then expanded in a power series in signal strength, and it was argued that the quadratic term should dominate. The figure of merit used was the SNR for the log-likelihood or for just the quadratic term. In reference [7], by contrast, the ideal-observer test statistic was taken as the likelihood, and it was shown that all terms in a power-series expansion for the likelihood gave useful discrimination; one could not drop the linear term or terms higher than quadratic without significant error. Moreover, the SNR for the likelihood was shown to behave in a very surprising way: it went through a maximum as signal strength increased and then approached zero. The behavior of d_a with signal strength was monotonic, so the authors of reference [7] entered a strong warning against SNR measures and in favor of d_a.

We have recently reinvestigated this problem in light of the results given earlier in this paper. Using a Monte Carlo procedure similar to that described in [7], we computed the means and variances of both the likelihood ratio and its logarithm under both hypotheses. The results for 128 locations and 5000 Monte Carlo samples are plotted in Fig. 1 as a function of a normalized signal contrast, defined so that a value of 1 would correspond to $d_a = 1$ if there were no location uncertainty. Of note is the huge variation in the means and variances of Λ; the signal-present variance covers some twenty orders of magnitude for a modest range of signal contrast, and the signal-absent variance covers five orders of magnitude. The signal-absent mean is always unity, in accord with (19), and (20) is also confirmed.

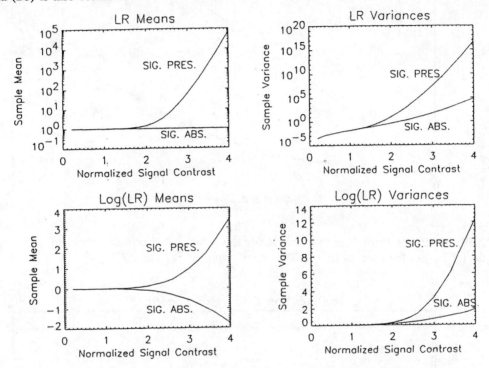

Fig. 1. Results of a Monte Carlo study of the moments of Λ and λ for detection of a known signal in white Gaussian noise, where the signal can be at 1 of 128 equally probable locations. The moments were computed from 5000 image samples.

The Monte Carlo moments for λ are much better behaved. They do not, however, agree with constraints derived in Sec. 3.4, so we must conclude that λ is not normally distributed. This conclusion is verified by computing histograms of λ for the Monte Carlo run, where an obvious skew is noted.

In spite of the non-Gaussian charcter of λ, SNR_λ is a reasonable figure of merit. Shown in Fig. 2 is a plot of d_a and SNR_λ from the Monte Carlo run as a function of signal strength. The two quantities agree fairly well with each other, and both are monotonic with signal strength. The nonmonotonic behavior of SNR_Λ, first noted in [7], is confirmed by our study and also plotted in Fig. 2. One conlcusion from this figure is that it can indeed be dangerous to use SNR as a figure of merit, but one is apparently much safer with SNR_λ than with SNR_Λ. The reason for this difference can be seen by referring again to Fig. 1; the rapid increase in $\mathrm{var}_1(\Lambda)$ with contrast is what drives SNR_Λ to zero. Neither λ nor Λ is normally distributed, but with Λ the deviations from normality are enormous.

Figure 3 is similar to Fig. 2 except that SNR_Λ has been deleted (as it should be) and $\sqrt{2G(0)}$, denoted $SNR[G(0)]$, has been added. It is seen that the likelihood-generating function at the origin is an excellent predictor of d_a and hence AUC.

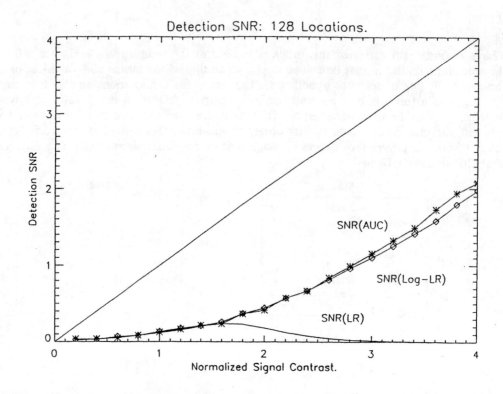

Fig. 2. Illustration of three figures of merit for the location-uncertainty problem. Shown are d_a as derived from the area under the ROC curves and SNR_Λ and SNR_λ.

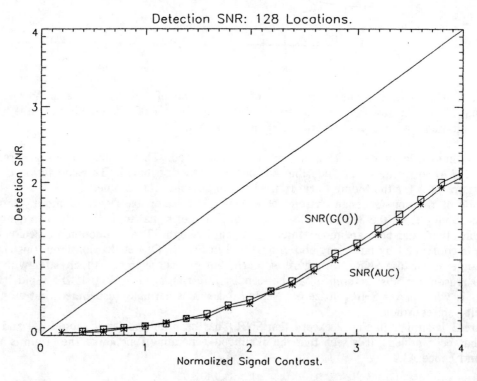

Fig. 3. Illustration of three figures of merit for the location-uncertainty problem. Shown now are d_a, SNR_λ and our newly proposed figure of merit, $\sqrt{2G(0)}$ or SNR[$G(0)$].

6. SUMMARY AND CONCLUSIONS

This paper has summarized the more detailed and mathematical treatment of [4] on statistical properties of the test statistics used by an ideal observer. In addition, it illustrated the applicability of these results to an interesting problem in signal detection, namely detection of a signal which is exactly known except for location.

Future work will apply the formalism to such problems as detection of a random or nonrandom signal in speckle or on log-normally distributed backgrounds. The goal will continue to be to expand the repertoire of problems for which we can compute the performance of the ideal observer and hence the efficiency of a human observer relative to the ideal.

ACKNOWLEDGEMENTS

The authors have benefitted from discussions with Kyle Myers, Robert Wagner, David Brown, Michael Insana, Charles Metz and Richard Swensson. This work was supported by the National Institutes of Health (NIH) through grant no. RO1 CA52643, but it does not represent an official position of NIH.

REFERENCES

1. H. H. Barrett, C. K. Abbey and Brandon Gallas, "Stabilized estimates of Hotelling-observer detection performance in patient-structured noise", Proc. SPIE 3340, 1998.

2. H. L. Van Trees, *Detection, Estimation, and Modulation Theory*, Vol. *I* (John Wiley, New York, 1968).

3. J. L. Melsa and D. L. Cohn, *Decision and Estimation Theory* (McGraw Hill, New York, 1978).

4. H. H. Barrett, C. K. Abbey and Eric Clarkson, "Objective assessment of image quality III: ROC metrics, ideal observers and likelihood-generating functions", accepted for publication in J. Opt. Soc. Am. *A*.

5. D. M. Green and J. A. Swets, *Signal Detection Theory and Psychophysics* (Wiley, New York, 1966).

6. H. H. Barrett, K. J. Myers and R. F. Wagner "Beyond signal-detection theory" Proc. SPIE 626:231-239, 1986.

7. D. G. Brown, M. F. Insana and M. Tapiovaara, "Detection performance of the ideal desicion function and its Maclaurin expansion", J. Acoust. Soc. Am. 97:379-392, 1995.

Comparing Observer Performance With Mixture Distribution Analysis When There Is No External Gold Standard

Harold L. Kundel [a] and Marcia Polansky [b]

[a] University of Pennsylvania, Philadelphia, PA 19104
[b] Allegheny University, Philadelphia, PA 19104

ABSTRACT

Mixture distribution analysis (MDA) is proposed as a statistical methodology for comparing observer readings on different imaging modalities when the image findings cannot be independently verified. The study utilized a data set consisting of independent, blinded readings by 4 radiologists of a stratified sample of 95 bedside chest images obtained using computed radiography. Each case was read on hard and soft copy. The area under the ROC curve (AUC) was calculated using ROCFIT and the relative percent correct (RPC) was calculated from point distributions estimated by the MDA. The expectation maximization (EM) algorithm was used to perform a maximum likelihood estimation of the fit to either 3, 4, or 5 point distributions. There was agreement between the AUC and the RPC based upon 3 point distributions representing easy normals, hard normals and abnormals, easy abnormals. Exploration of the data sets also showed good correlation with 4 point distributions representing easy normals, hard normals, hard abnormals and easy abnormals. We conclude that the MDA may be a viable alternative to the ROC for evaluating observer performance on imaging modalities in clinical settings where image verification is either difficult or impossible.

Keywords: observer performance, mixture distribution analysis, receiver operating characteristic analysis, ROC, chest images, computed radiography

1. BACKGROUND

1.1 Laboratory vs. clinical studies of imaging technology

Objective studies comparing the performance of imaging systems can be carried out in the laboratory or in the clinic. Laboratory studies are advantageous because the testing conditions and the image content can be controlled. The studies can be designed to take advantage of the receiver operating characteristic (ROC) analysis, which is considered to be the most powerful statistical methodology available for comparing diagnostic systems (1, 2).

Caution must be exercised when trying to apply the results of a laboratory study to a clinical population because selection and verification bias (3) may have resulted in a sample that does not represent the clinical population from which the cases were drawn. A proper ROC analysis requires that the cases be dichotomized into diseased and disease-free categories by a method independent of the imaging procedure being studied. Therefore, only verified cases can be included in the test set. Many clinical cases cannot be independently verified. The ROC analysis also requires the readers to distribute their responses over a rating scale. A typical five level scale consists of the following responses: 1) definitely positive, 2) probably positive, 3) possibly positive, 4) probably negative and 5) definitely negative. The readers must be willing to use all of the response categories and the cases must be sufficiently difficult to allow a spread of the responses over the rating scale (4). At least a few "definitely positive" responses are desirable for the disease-free cases. To achieve this either difficult or ambiguous disease-free cases must be selected (5).

SPIE Vol. 3340 • 0277-786X/98/$10.00

1.2 Comparing imaging systems by using stress tests

Mindful of selection and verification bias, the usual approach to a laboratory study is to develop a stress test. For chest imaging a test set might be composed of cases with specific diagnostic findings such as pneumothoraces or nodules that are considered to represent the most difficult diagnostic situations likely to be encountered in chest radiography. Frequently, confusing cases without pneumothoraces and nodules are selected as disease-free controls. It is reasoned that if two imaging modalities result in the same performance on such difficult diagnostic findings, they will be the same on everything else. Most comparisons of hard and soft copy readings of chest images have used stress tests (6-11).

1.3 Difficulties of comparing imaging systems using field tests

Any representative sample of clinical cases will includes cases that cannot be independently verified. For example, there may be disagreement about whether there is malposition of a tube or catheter on a bedside chest image. The position could be proved by a CT scan (which may be impossible on a very sick patient) but it is better to assume the worst case and move the tube. If this image is selected for inclusion in a study, a ruling about the position of the tube can be made by a single expert or by a panel of experts. However, experts can be wrong. Revesz et al. (12) have shown that the method of verifying the cases for an ROC analysis can significantly alter the results of a comparison of imaging techniques. The truth determined by a panel can be at odds with the truth determined by surgical pathology and the truth determined by the panel can even vary depending upon the method used for arriving at agreement. In addition, an expert panel is very labor intensive and can make as many as 3 experts ineligible to act as readers.

1.4 Comparing imaging system performance using measures of agreement

The indeterminate nature of panel derived truth led us to look at methods for comparing performance that did not require the rigorous determination of truth. Henkelman et al. (13) proposed a method for estimating the truth for an ROC analysis from the data obtained from three imaging modalities (radionuclide scanning, magnetic resonance imaging, computed tomography) performed on the same cases. However, as Revesz et al. (12) and Begg and Metz (14) point out, a consensus can only approximate the ground truth. The greater the intrinsic accuracy of the imaging procedure, the closer the consensus comes to the ground truth.

Rather than trying to use consensus to estimate accuracy, we decided to use a measure of agreement. We wanted a measure that had an intuitive meaning and that could be used in both paired and unpaired studies. The kappa statistic was considered inappropriate because of the difficulty in interpreting its meaning. Consider, two reasons for ordering images in a medical intensive care unit, namely, checking the position of tubes and catheters and diagnosing congestive heart failure. A chest image is always obtained to determine if a central venous catheter is properly positioned because a malpositioned catheter can lead to devastating complications. Congestive heart failure (CHF) is a much more difficult and controversial diagnosis. It occurs in about half of the patients. A comparison of 2 readers on 100 cases of each is shown in Table 1. The kappa is .66 for tubes and catheters and .68 for congestive heart failure. It seems odd to get the same value for kappa when the uncorrected agreement for tubes and catheters is 98% and for CHF is 84%. The reason is the difference in the prevalence malpositioned tubes and CHF (5% vs. 50%) and the sensitivity of the radiographic examination (high vs. medium). Fortunately for our patients, 96% of catheters are correctly placed and the chance that an image will show correct placement is over 90%. As a consequence the correction for chance is large and the kappa is low.

Aicken (15) tried to apply a correction by assuming that there were two types of agreement, agreement by cause and agreement by chance. In the context of imaging, he was postulating two kinds of cases, easy cases where agreement was likely to be very high and hard cases where genuine guessing occurred. He proposed a method for first removing the easy cases and then calculated a statistic called alpha on the hard cases. The value of Aickin's alpha, which is more intuitive than kappa, is shown in Table 1. Notice that when the prevalence is 50% the value of alpha is about the same as kappa but when the prevalence is 2% the value of alpha is greater than kappa.

Table 1 The agreement on a hypothetical sample of 100 chest images made to determine the position of tubes and catheters and 100 images made to diagnose congestive heart failure.

	Tubes and Catheters			Congestive Heart Failure	
	R1	R2		R1	R2
R1	2	1	R1	42	8
R2	1	96	R2	8	42

agreement (uncor) = .98	agreement (uncor) = .84
kappa = .66	kappa = .68
alpha = .89	alpha = .67

Aikins approach is a form of mixture distribution analysis (16, 17). In MDA we assume that we have a sample of cases from a population that contains a mixture of four kinds of case: easy normals, hard normals, hard diseased, and easy diseased. An easy normal is a case that about 95% of all expert readers would agree is normal and a hard normal is a case that only about 50% of expert readers would agree is normal. The same applies to diseased cases. The objective of the analysis is to use the sample to estimate the composition of the population. Each of the 4 distributions has at least two parameters: the proportion of the total cases p_i in that class and the proportion of readers that agree about the diagnosis m_i. Table 2 shows a hypothetical mixture of 4 distributions.

Table 2 The distribution of cases and readings in a hypothetical population.

Class	Proportion of Cases (p)	Proportion of Agreement Among a Large Group of Expert Readers (m)	p*m
Easy Normal	.4	.95	.38
Hard Normal	.2	.60	.12
Hard Abnormal	.15	.55	.08
Easy Abnormal	.25	.96	.24
Totals	1.0		.82

The sum of the product p*m x 100 is called the relative percent agreement (RPA) and it is the summary measure of performance that we use. This statistic indicates the proportion of the time that a typical reader would agree with the majority of all readers.

2. METHODS

2.1 The image reading study

A stratified sample of 95 bedside chest radiographs made using computed radiography was selected from the cases obtained in a 16 bed medical intensive care unit (MICU). The cases were selected on the basis of the reason for requesting the examination. All of the images were made using computed radiography. The hard copy images were printed on an LP400 laser printer (Sterling Imaging, Wilmington,DE). The soft copy images were displayed at 1684 x 2048 pixels on a workstation using two Megascan monitors (AVP/E Systems Boston,MA). The images were verified for an ROC analysis by a panel of 3 radiologists with access to clinical information and other images. The hard and soft copy images were read by 4 chest radiologists who were not on the verification panel.

The readers were give the reason for requesting the examination (for example rule-out pneumonia) and were asked to respond to the question implied by the reason using a five level confidence scale. The scale was as follows: 1) definitely positive, 2) probably positive, 3) possibly positive, 4) probably negative, 5 definitely negative. The details have been published along with the ROC analysis (18).

2.2 The receiver operating characteristic (ROC) analysis

The cases were dichotomized into normal and abnormal on the basis of the panel decision. The rating data for each individual were averaged and the program ROCFIT was used to determine the area under the curve (AUC) and the standard error (SE). The 95% confidence intervals were calculated as $1.96 \pm SE$.

2.3 The mixture distribution analysis

The ratings were dichotomized by considering 1,2 and 3 as positive and 4 and 5 as negative. The parameters of 3 point distributions (easy normals, easy abnormals and hard normals and abnormals combined) were calculated using the binomial distribution.

The probability that r out of n readers report as positive an image that it is randomly selected from all of the images is

$$\text{Prob} = \Sigma \ (\ p_i \ n! \ / \ (n-r)! \ r! \ ) \quad m_i^r \ (1-m_i)^{n-r} \tag{1}$$

where m_i is the probability that a large number of readers concludes "positive" for each group and p_i is the proportion of images falling in each group. The EM algorithm (19) was used to do a maximum likelihood estimation of the proportion p_i of images falling into each group and to estimate the probability m_i of a large number of readers concluding that the images in that group are positive. The 95% confidence intervals were calculated using a bootstrapping technique (20). The details of this approach have been published (21).

3. RESULTS

The summary data are shown in Table 3 as the mean of the RPA and the AUC along with 95% confidence intervals.

Table 3 The relative percent agreement (RPA) and the area under the ROC curve (AUC) given as mean and (95% confidence interval).

Display	RPA	AUC
Hard-Copy	78 (72 - 86)	78 (76 - 80)
Soft-Copy	79 (74 - 87)	81 (76 - 88)

The parameters of the three point distributions are shown in Table 4.

Table 4 The probability (m_i) of a large number of readers agreeing about the images in a group and the proportion (p_i) of images falling into each group.

Display	Easy Abnormals		Hard Combined		Easy Normals	
	m_1	p_1	m_2	p_2	m_3	p_3
Hard-Copy	86	19	44	25	95	56
Soft-Copy	99	10	47	42	99	47

The data from hard and soft copy were combined so that there were 8 readings per image and the MDA was run assuming that there were 3, 4 or 5 point distributions. The results are shown in Table 5 as the probability of a large group of readers agreeing that the image is POSITIVE. Note that this is not the way the data in Tables 4 and 5 were presented. Agreement that an image is negative is 1- agreement that it is positive. Additionally, the data are arranged hierarchically. Going from 3 to 4 distributions results in a loss of the distribution at 43. The distributions are plotted in Figure 1.

Table 5   The probability (m_i) of a large number of readers agreeing about the images in a group is positive and the proportion (p_i) of images falling into each group.

Number of Distributions	Easy Abnormal				Hard Combined				Easy Normals			
	m_1	p_1	m_2	p_2	m_3	p_3	m_4	p_4	m_5	p_5	m_6	p_6
3	97	12	--	--	43	40	--	--	04	48	--	--
4	99	9	67	16	--	--	27	39	01	36	--	--
5	100	9	71	14	--	--	29	38	03	6	01	34

Figure 1   Plots of the data in Table 5 showing the effect of using 3 (A) , 4 (B) or 5(C) point distributions in the analysis.

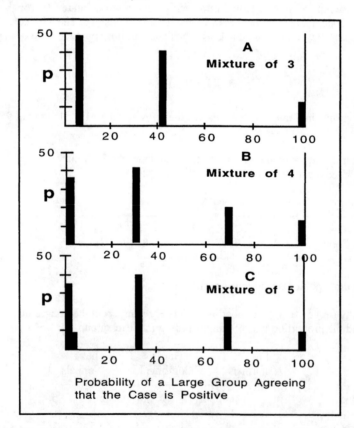

4. DISCUSSION

The difference in the RPA between hard and soft copy readings (78 to 81) is not significant but examination of the parameters shows that going from hard to soft copy has resulted in a shift in cases from the two easy groups to the single hard group (25% to 42%). At the same time the percent agreement (m) on the remaining easy cases has become greater (86 to 99 for abnormals and 95 to 99 for normals). At present we have no method for testing the statistical significance of the shifts but we are working on a paired analysis that will allow us to do such testing.

It is possible that there are more than 3 underlying distributions. Having 4 readers only gives us enough degrees of freedom to compute 3 distributions. However, analysis of the combined hard and soft copy readings (Table 5 Figure 1) show that although there may be 4 there are not 5 distributions.

It may not be fair to compare the MDA with an ROC analysis that used a panel as the final arbiter of truth. The panel may just act as a super expert. We need to test the technique against a set of cases in which the verification was made by a relatively independent method such as biopsy or surgery. On the other hand, eliminating the need for a verification panel frees up experts for use as readers and broadens the ability to select cases.

5. ACKNOWLEDGMENTS

This work was supported by Grant CA 53141 from the NCI, USPHS, DHHS.
The authors are grateful to Drs. Aronchick, Gefter, Hatabu, Miller,Jr, Miller,Sr. and Whitfill for reading images and acting as panelists.

6. REFERENCES

1. Swets JA. Measuring the accuracy of diagnostic systems. Science 1988;240:1285-1293.
2. Dorfman DD, Berbaum KS, Metz CE. Receiver operating characteristic analysis. Generalization to the population of readers and patients with the jackknife method. Invest Radiol 1992;27:723-731.
3. Begg CB, McNeil BJ. Assessment of radiologic tests: Control of bias and other design considerations. Radiology 1988;167:565-569.
4. Revesz G, Kundel HL. The evaluation of radiographic technoques by observer tests: Problems, pitfalls and procedures. Invest Radiol 1974;9:166-173.
5. Gur D, King JL, Rockette HE, Britton CA, Thaete FL, Hoy RJ. Practical issues of experimental ROC analysis. Invest Radiol 1989;25:583-586.
6. Slasky BS, Gur D, Good WF, et al. Receiver operating characteristic analysis of chest image interpretation with conventional, laser printed, and high-resolution workstation images. Radiology 1990;174:775-780.
7. Brown JJ, Malchow SC, Totty WG, et al. MR examination of the knee: Interpretation with multiscreen digital workstation vs hardcopy format. AJR 1991;157:81-85.
8. MacMahon H, Metz CE, Doi K, Kim T, Giger ML, Chan HP. Digital chest radiography: Effect of diagnostic accuracy of hard copy, conventional video, and reversed gray scale video display formats. Radiology 1988;168:669-673.
9. Razavi M, Sayre JW, Taira R, et al. Receiver-operating-characteristic study of chest radiographs in children: Digital hard-copy film vs 2K x 2K soft-copy images. AJR 1992;158:443-448.
10. Cox GG, Cook LT, McMillan JH, Rosenthal SJ, Dwyer SJ. Chest radiography: Comparison of high-resolution digital displays with conventional and digital film. Radiology 1990;176:771-776.
11. Scott WW, Rosenbaum JE, Ackerman SJ, et al. Subtle orthopedic fractures: Teleradiology workstation versus film interpretation. Radiology 1993;187:811-815.
12. Revesz G, Kundel HL, Bonitatibus M. The effect of verification on the assessment of imaging techniques. Invest Radiol 1983;18(2):194-198.
13. Henkelman RM, Kay I, Bronskill MJ. Receiver operating characteristic (ROC) analysis without truth. Medic Decis Making 1990;10:24-29.
14. Begg CB, Metz CE. Consensus diagnoses and "gold standards". Medic Decis Making 1990;10:29-30.
15. Aickin M. Maximum likelihood estimation of agreement in the constant predictive probability model, and its relation to Cohen's kappa. Biometrics 1990;46:293-302.

16. Uebersax JS. Statistical modeling of expert ratings on medical treatment appropriateness. Journal of the American Statistical Association 1993;88:421-427.

17. Titterington DM, Smith AFM, Makov UE. Statistical Analysis of Finite Mixture Distributions.New York: John Wiley & Sons, 1985

18. Kundel H, Gefter W, Aronchick J, et al. Relative accuracy of screen-film and computed radiography using hard and soft copy readings: A receiver operating characteristic analysis using bedside chest radiographs in a medical intensive care unit. Radiology 1997;205:859-863.

19. Dempster A, Laird N, Rubin D. Maximum likelihood from incomplete data via the EM algorithm. J R Stat Soc 1977;B39:1-38.

20. Efron B. Better bootstrap confidence intervals. J Amer Statistical Assn 1987;82:171-200.

21. Kundel HL, Polansky M. Mixture distribution and receiver operating characteristic analysis of bedside chest imaging using screen-film and computed radiography. Academic Radiology 1997;4:1-7.

Synthesis of biomedical tissue

Jannick P. Rolland[a], , Alexei Goon[a], Eric Clarkson[b], and Liyun Yu[a]

[a]School of Optics and CREOL, UCF
[b]Optical Sciences Center, University of Arizona

ABSTRACT

Image quality assessment in medical imaging requires realistic textured backgrounds that can be statistically characterized for the computation of model observers' performance. We present a modeling framework for the synthesis of texture as well as a statistical analysis of both sample and synthesized textures. The model employs a two-component image-decomposition consisting of a slowly, spatially varying mean-background and a residual texture image. Each component is synthesized independently. The technique is demonstrated using radiological breast tissue. For statistical characterization, we compute the two-point probability density functions for the real and synthesized breast tissue textures in order to provide a complete characterization and comparison of their second-order statistics. Similar computations for other textures yield further insight into the statistical properties of these types of random fields.

Keywords: textured backgrounds; random fields; medical backgrounds; texture synthesis; first and second order statistics.

1. INTRODUCTION

Medical and biomedical imaging research aims at developing better imaging systems, more accurate reconstructions, and methods of image processing and analysis that utilize the most important information present in an image for accurate and timely diagnosis of disease. Realistic numerical models of human tissue and medical imaging systems are key components to achieving this goal. This paper specifically addresses an approach to the modeling of biological tissue, where the technique is demonstrated for radiological breast tissue, also referred to as mammographic tissue.

The method for synthesis decomposes an image into a slowly, spatially varying mean-background and a residual texture image.[1-3] We shall refer to the slowly, spatially varying mean-background as the mean background. The texture image can be successfully synthesized using a multi-scale multi-orientation framework based on the steerable pyramid transform. While we proposed in an earlier paper to model the mean background as a stochastic process known as the lumpy background,[3-6] we have encouraging results showing that those slowly, spatially varying backgrounds may also be synthesized with the framework used to synthesize the finer underlying texture.

A useful synthesis framework for medical imaging research is one that can yield images with known statistical properties. As a first step to characterize the statistical properties of textured backgrounds, we propose to estimate the first and second order statistics as the one-point and the two-point probability density functions that characterize completely their first and second-order statistics.

2. A COMPLEX BACKGROUND AS A TWO COMPONENT MODEL

Radiologic breast tissue samples appear as if they are formed as the superimposition of a slowly, spatially varying background and a finer texture image. Thus we propose to decompose them in these two components. A typical decomposition is shown in Fig. 1. The slowly, spatially varying background referred as the mean background is obtained by filtering the original mammogramm image with a Gaussian kernel with a standard deviation of six pixels. The residual texture image is the difference between the image and the mean background.

It can be noted from Fig.1 that the mean background resembles lumpy backgrounds.[5-6] In the literature on image quality assessment for medical imaging, lumpy backgrounds are considered to be useful models of anatomical variations because: 1. They account for background variability and 2. In one type of lumpy backgrounds the probability density is known to be multivariate Gaussian while in the other the covariance matrix is known to be Gaussian. Knowledge of the covariance matrix has made possible the computation of various predictive models of image quality assessment for the detection of lesions in such backgrounds.[4] Knowledge of the full probability density functions allows computation of the ideal observer.

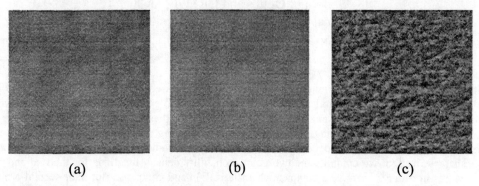

(a)　　　　　　　　　(b)　　　　　　　　　(c)

Fig.1. Mammography breast image decomposition: (a) The original sample. (b) The slowly, spatially varying mean-background. (c) The residual texture image.

3. A FRAMEWORK FOR TEXTURE SYNTHESIS

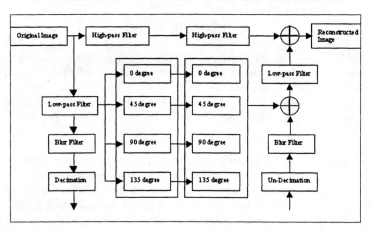

Fig.2. Illustration of one level of the steerable pyramid transform used in the texture synthesis algorithm. The input image in the upper left corner would be either the texture sample or the white noise image. A synthesis is obtained by recombination of the decomposed noise image through the right hand side of the pyramid.

The algorithm for texture synthesis we propose is based on a multiple scale decomposition of a sample texture image and the same decomposition of a realization of a uniformly distributed white noise image. The algorithm is composed of four essential components: the pyramid transform, the image decomposition, the histogram matching procedure, and the texture synthesis. The algorithm was implemented in IDL language and is best described by considering the four individual components:

The Pyramid Transform: The proposed algorithm for the synthesis of the residual texture is based on a four-layer steerable pyramid transform. One layer of the pyramid is depicted in Fig. 2. Layers are connected by a factor-of-two downsampling also known as decimation of the image.[7-8] Within each layer, the image is filtered by a set of bandpass filters and followed by a set of orientation filters that form a quadrature mirror filter bank.[7-10] A four (scales) by four (orientations: 0 degree, 45 degree, 90 degree and 135 degree) 17x17 size filters were adopted.

Image Decomposition: The texture image is processed through the left-hand side of the pyramid transform shown in Fig. 2. It is represented in Fig. 2 as an input to the pyramid in the upper left corner. In parallel, a realization of uniformly distributed white noise, referred thereafter as white noise, is also processed by the same pyramid transform, that is, it is also fed independently to the pyramid transform in the upper left corner. The role of the white noise image is to provide a starting point for the synthesis.

Histogram matching at multiple scales: After decomposition of a texture sample and a realization image of white noise, the histograms of the subband images (i.e. output images of the filters on the left hand side of the pyramid) of the texture image and of the noise image are matched.[11,12] Histogram matching is an image processing technique, specifically a point operation, which modifies a candidate image so that its histogram matches that of a model image.[13-14]

Texture Synthesis: The histogram-matched noise subband-images obtained at multiple scales are then recombined according to the right-hand side of the pyramid transform shown in Fig. 2. The synthesis operation is a blurring between scales. Moreover, the greylevels of the undecimated image must be multiplied by a factor of four at each stage of the synthesis to account for the loss in brightness the image did undergo upon decimation by a level of two. This process repeated at multiple scales yields a synthetic image. If another realization of white noise is processed instead, the synthesis yields another realization of the synthesized image.

4. SYNTHESIS OF MAMMOGRAPHIC BREAST TISSUE SAMPLES

The framework described was applied to the synthesis of both the residual texture component and the mean background. Two synthesis realizations of the residue image are shown in the two rightmost images in Fig. 3. Each synthesis corresponds to a new realization of white noise as a starting point. On the left, a realization of the noise is shown which is followed to the right by the residual texture.

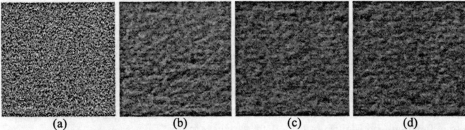

(a)	(b)	(c)	(d)

Fig. 3. Syntheses of a residual mammographic texture image: (a) a typical sample of a uniformly distributed white noise image used as a starting point for one synthesis; (b) original mammographic residual texture; (c) synthesis1; (d) synthesis 2.

5. SYNTHESIS OF THE MEAN BACKGROUND

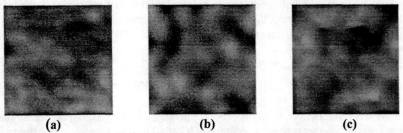

(a)	(b)	(c)

Fig. 4. Models of the mean background. (a) sample mean-background extracted from a mammogram; (b) a model using a lumpy background; (c) a model using the steerable pyramid transform to synthesize the background.

In an earlier paper, we proposed to model the mean background as the lumpy background, a wide-sense stationary random process established for image quality assessment in medical imaging.[3] In later investigations backgrounds synthesised with the steerable pyramid transform more closely matched the sample than those generated by the lumpy background process. The new synthesized backgrounds are shown in Fig. 4.

6. A PROPOSED MATHEMATICAL PHANTOM

The synthesis of an ensemble of images $M_i(x,y)$ according to the described mathematical phantom can be established using an adaptive linear combination of realizations from the two model components: a realization of the mean background component denoted as $L_i(x,y)$ and a realization of the synthesized texture component denoted as $T_i(x,y)$. The resulting synthesized image will then be given by

$$M_i(x,y) = \beta \ L_i(x,y) + (1-\beta) \ T_i(x,y) \ , \qquad (1)$$

where β ranges from 0 to 1. Such a combination will allow us to span a wide range of tissue types with relative amounts of mean and textured backgrounds. We hypothesize that by such a combination, various tissue types as described by Wolfe for example can be synthesized.[15] On a more theoretical basis, one can also study a wide range of combinations of such backgrounds by varying β and the texture samples associated with each component. Such a framework may naturally find application to a wide range of complex backgrounds.

7. FIRST AND SECOND-ORDER STATISTICS

While the original mammogram image and the mean background are non-stationary random processes, the extracted residual texture-image appears stationary. In fact, while we do not know whether it is stationary, we shall assume such property based on perceptual estimation. Furthermore, it is important to note that the proposed synthesis framework, that matches first-order statistics of subband images, would yield artifacts while synthesizing a non-stationary random process as a consequence of inhomogeneities in the texture.[11] Therefore, the success in synthesizing a given texture sample yields insight into the stationarity property of the sample texture.

By construction, a sample and its synthesis have equal first-order statistics. The next level of description of a random field is its second-order statistics. Second-order statistics are fully described by the two-point probability density function (2P-PDF). For a stationary random process, one component of the 2P-PDF can be estimated by the co-occurrence of two greylevels for any two pixels separated by a fixed vector **d** in the sample image. Computations of components of the 2P-PDF as **d** varies are shown in Fig. 5 and 6 for the mammographic texture and a granite texture. For the original residual texture sample, Fig 5 shows that its 2P-PDF is extremely similar to that of a synthesis of that sample. Quantification of the similarity between two PDFs can be estimated by the root mean-square distance between the two functions and is given in Table 1 for various textures.

It is critical to note that this distance measure is only meaningful between functions describing textures whose first-order statistics have been matched. Therefore, we chose to match the first-order statistics of all textures to that of the residue image. The 2P-PDFs were then computed and the measure of distance computed. Fig. 6 shows the 2P-PDFs for a granite-texture sample and the same texture after the first-order statistics have been matched to that of the residual texture image. We note that first-order statistics play a key role in the shape of the second order statistics. It is a question of investigation weather or not the measure of distance between two 2P-PDFs heavily depends on the first-order statistics. Future work will further explore properties of 2P-PDFs and investigate models of detection in textured backgrounds using such statistics.

8. CONCLUSION

We presented a framework for texture synthesis and application to mammographic breast tissue samples. A key component to the successful synthesis of such complex backgrounds was to decompose the radiologic tissue sample into a slowly, varying mean-background and a finer scale texture. Each component was successfully synthesized independently. Finally, we presented a complete analysis of the second order statistics of the residual texture image that prompted us with stimulating future work on texture characterization.

9. ACKNOWLEDGEMENTS

We thank Harry Barrett for stimulating discussions about the two-point probability density function. We also thank Kyle Myers for stimulating discussions about texture analysis and Art Burgess for discussions about some of the literature on mammography. This work was supported in part by a small grant from the University of Central Florida.

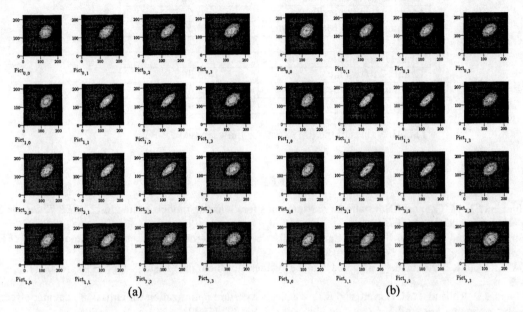

Fig. 5. The two-point probability density functions for (a) the residue texture image; and (b) a synthesis of the residual image. Each function within an image corresponds to a different value of the vector **d**. From left to right, **d** equal (-5,5); (-3,5); (3,5); (5,5). From top to bottom **d** equal (-5,5);(-5;3);(-5,-3);(-5,5).

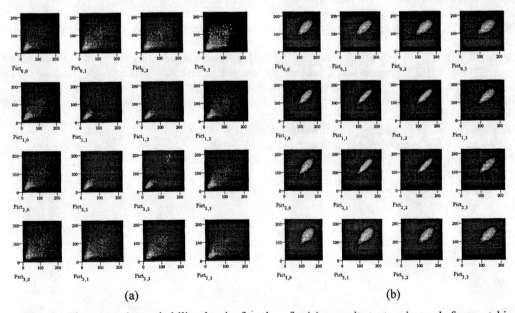

Fig. 6. The two-point probability density functions for (a) a granite texture image before matching of the first-order statistics to that of the residue image; and (b) after matching of the first-order statistics to that of the residue image. The values of **d** are the same as described in Fig.5.

Textures	Distance
Mammo-syn1 to residue	0.618
Mammo-syn2 to residue	0.621
Mammo-syn3 to residue	0.623
Mammo-syn1 to Mammo-syn2	0.538
Granite1 to residue	2.370
Granite2 to residue	3.386
Granite3 to residue	2.487
Grass to residue	2.438

Table1. Values of the RMS distance between two 2P-PDFs.

10. REFERENCES

1. B.R. Hunt, and T. M. Cannon, "Nonstationary assumptions for Gaussian models of images," *IEEE Trans. on Sys., Man, and Cybern.,* 876-882 (1976).
2. R.N. Strickland, and H.I. Hahn, "Wavelet transforms for detecting microcalcifications in mammograms," *IEEE Trans. on Med. Imaging* **15**, 218-229 (1996).
3. Rolland, J.P., and R. Strickland, "An approach to the synthesis of biological tissue," Optics Express, 1(13), 414-423 (1997).
4. K.J. Myers, J.P. Rolland, H.H. Barrett, and R.F. Wagner, "Aperture optimization for emission imaging: effect of a spatially varying background," *J. Opt. Soc. Am. A.* **7**, 1279-1293 (1990).
5. J.P. Rolland, "Factors influencing lesion detection in medical imaging," Ph.D. Dissertation, University of Arizona, (1990).
6. J.P. Rolland, and H.H. Barrett, "Effect of random background inhomogeneity on observer detection performance," *J. Opt. Soc. Am. A.* **9**, 649-658 (1992).
7. P.P. Vaidyanathan. *Multivariate systems and filter banks.* (Prentice Hall, NJ, 1993).
8 J. W. Woods. *Subband Image Coding.* (Kluwer Academic Publishers, MA, 1991).
9. W.T. Freeman and E.H. Adelson, "The design and use of steerable filters," IEEE Pat. Anal. Mach. Intell., 13(9), 891-906 (1991).
10. E.P. Simoncelli, and W.T. Freeman, "The steerable pyramid: a flexible architecture for multi-scale derivative computation," Proc. of IEEE International Conference on Image Processing, Washington DC, November (1995).
11. D.J. Heeger, and J.R. Bergen, "Pyramid-based texture analysis/synthesis," *Compt. Graph.* 229-238 (1995).
12. J.P. Rolland, V. Vo, C.K. Abbey, L. Yu, and B. Bloss, "An optimal algorithm for histogram matching: application to texture synthesis," (in press).
13. W.K. Pratt, *Digital Image Processing.* (John Wiley & Sons, NY, 1991).
14. K.R. Castleman, *Digital Image Processing.* (Prentice Hall, NJ, 1996).
15. J.N. Wolfe, "Breast patterns as an index of risk for developing breast cancer," *Am. J. Roentgenol.* 126, 1130-1139 (1976).

SESSION 2

Practical Aspects of Perception

Effect of image processing on diagnostic decisions in chest radiography

Elizabeth Krupinski and Michael Evanoff

Department of Radiology, University of Arizona, Tucson, AZ 85724

ABSTRACT

The goal of this study was to determine what the influence of image processing functions was on decisions and decision changes made while reading chest radiographs displayed on a monitor. Six radiologists read 168 computed radiography chest images first without then with the use of six image processing functions. Diagnostic performance was measured using Receiver Operating Characteristic analysis, and decision changes made without and with processing use were analyzed. Diagnostic performance did not differ statistically for readings without and with image processing. The decision change analysis showed that readers were just as likely to change decisions from true-positive to false-negative as they were from false-negative to true-positive. With image processing, there were significantly more changes from true-negative to false-positive than from false-positive to true-negative. 93% of all decisions did not change with the use of image processing. No significant correlations were found between the type of lesions present on the radiograph and the type of image processing function used. Positive decision changes made with the use of image processing are offset by equivalent numbers of negative decision changes. The use of image processing does not affect significantly diagnostic performance in chest radiography.

Keywords : observer performance, image processing, decision changes, ROC analysis

1. INTRODUCTION

As the use of computers increases in the practice of radiology (e.g., for PACS and teleradiology), different ways of processing images for display on computer monitors are being investigated. Key to having these image processing functions used successfully in the clinical environment is demonstrating that they either improve diagnostic accuracy or at least improve the general appearance of the image so that radiologists like the way the images look on the monitor. Ideally, image processing should improve the diagnostic accuracy and confidence of the radiologist.[1] The results of studies aimed at demonstrating this improved accuracy and confidence with image processing have, however, produced equivocal results.[2,3] Two possible reasons for equivocacy in experimental results may be that a) different image processing functions/algorithms are tested, and b) different types of images and disease entities may affect the effectiveness of a given processing algorithm. Therefore, it may be that there is no general set of processing functions that everyone can adopt for every situation. Specific processing functions may be more appropriate for different types of images and disease entities.

The goal of the present study was to determine the influence of a variety of image processing functions on diagnostic accuracy and types of decision changes made by radiologists reading images from a CRT monitor. For this particular study computed radiography chest images were used, since chest radiography is the most common type of exam performed in most radiology departments. Six image processing functions were developed, with the help of an experienced chest radiographer. A Receiver Operating Characteristic (ROC) study was performed to assess observer performance with and without image processing. Changes in decisions were analyzed as was the frequency of use of the various processing functions. An analysis was also performed to determine if specific image processing functions were used more often with particular disease entities than with other ones.

2. METHODS & MATERIALS

Computed radiography chest images (n = 168) were selected from cases at the Toshiba General Hospital (Tokyo, Japan) and the University of Arizona Departments of Radiology. 104 cases contained subtle nodules (n = 38), interstitial disease (n = 51) or bronchiectasis (n = 15) that were missed by the original reader and detected either in other exams (e.g., CT) or in retrospect. 64 of the cases were lesion-free with respect to chest pathologies. Six image

SPIE Vol. 3340 • 0277-786X/98/$10.00

processing functions were optimized for viewing chest images on a 2K x 2.5K monitor (MegaScan, Westford, MA). The six processing functions were : similar to film, lung window, mediastinum window, black & white reverse, low-pass and high-pass filters. "Raw" digital data (1760 x 2140), 10-bit processed converted to 8-bit for display, were used throughout. The monitor on which the images were displayed was perceptually linearized prior to the experiment. The "dark" luminance (light emitted from the monitor with no image displayed) was 0.02 foot-lamberts. The "maximum" luminance (average of the Society of Motion Picture and Television Engineers (SMPTE) pattern 100% values) was 88.50 foot-lamberts.

Six radiologists experienced in reading chest exams read the images.. For each image, the radiologists determined the diagnostic category (normal, nodule, interstitial, bronchiectasis) and reported their confidence in that decision using a 6-level rating scale. Readers gave two reports : the first without use of the presets (images appeared using the linear, film-like function); then they could use any of the presets and revise the original decision and confidence rating. The computer recorded each time any image processing function was used, and how long the radiologists took to diagnose each image. At the end of the study, the radiologists were asked to fill out a questionnaire rating each of the image processing presets (poor, fair, good, excellent) and overall image quality and resolution.

3. RESULTS

The image processing functions were rated as good or excellent by 4/6 readers for linear; 5/6 for lung; 4/6 for mediastinum; 5/6 for reverse; 1/6 for low-pass; and 5/6 for high-pass. All readers rated image resolution and overall image quality adequate for diagnosis. When asked how they would prefer the images to appear for the first time viewing, all readers preferred some combination of lung and the high-pass filter rather than the film-like linear image. On average the linear (film-like) processing function was used 1.29 times per image during the second decision phase; lung window 1.00 times on average; mediastinum 0.418 times on average; reverse 0.519 times on average; low-pass 0.042 times on average; and high-pass 0.568 times on average per image. For each of these processing functions, there were no differences in frequency of use between lesion types (i.e., used the same amount for nodule, interstitial, bronchiectasis and normal images). Figure 1 shows the average use of each processing function per image for each diagnostic category. It is apparent that there are no differences in which processing functions were used for the different diagnostic categories. The linear function was most preferred for all diagnostic categories and the low-pass was least preferred. Readers did not use a given processing function more often with one diagnostic category versus another.

The decision confidence ratings were used to generate Receiver Operating Characteristic (ROC) area under the curve (Az) values for the two conditions (reading without processing, reading with processing). The Multi-Reader Multi-Case ROC technique developed by Dorfman et al.[4] was used for the analysis. The average Az for the first reading without use of processing was 0.8558 (se = 0.0239), and the Az for the second reading with processing was 0.8536 (se = 0.0214). There was no statistically significant difference in diagnostic accuracy between the two reading conditions (Satterthwaite approximation for Analysis of Variance : df = 10, F = 0.0507, p = 0.8262). The ROC Az values and 95% confidence limits of the difference in Az values for the mean values and the individual readers can be found in Figure 2. There were no significant differences (p > 0.05) in Az for any of the individual readers with and without processing use. Separate analyses of the three diagnostic categories (nodule, interstitial, bronchiectasis) showed no significant differences in performance with and without processing use for any of the categories. The normal cases were randomized and proportionally split between the three categories to compute this analysis.

A paired sign test conducted on the confidence values for decisions without and with processing was statistically significant (z = 3.78, df = 1, p < .0001). Of the 1008 pairs of decisions (6 readers x 168 cases), 729 (72%) had no change in confidence, 79 (8%) went from a higher confidence (towards the definitely present or absent end of the scale) without processing to a lower confidence (towards the possibly present or absent end of the scale) with processing; and 200 (20%) went from a lower confidence without processing to a higher confidence with processing. The percent decision confidence changes for the individual diagnostic categories can be found in Figure 3. It is important to note that a change in confidence rating does not always reflect a change in decision. Actual decision changes are reported on below.

There was a total of 353 (35%) errors made out of the 1008 total decisions made by the 6 radiologists. A summary of the types of decisions made first without image processing and those made with image processing are presented in Figure 4. Categories above the dotted line are those where no change in decision occurred with image processing; those below the line are decisions that did change with processing. Only 7% of all the decisions made changed with image processing. Thirty-five percent of these change decisions involved an FN or FP decision error. The false-negative (FN) errors can be classified in two ways - omission errors (lesion present but not reported) or misclassification errors (lesion present and reported but classified as the wrong type of lesion). Twenty-one percent of all the decisions made were FN-FN. Of these FN-FN errors, 52% were misclassifications for both decisions; 40% were omissions for both decisions; 4% were missed on the first decision and misclassified on the second; and 4% were misclassified on the first decision and missed on the second. Only 2% of the total number of decisions were FN-TP (true-positive). Of these the FN was an omission 74% of the time and a misclassification 26% of the time. Likewise, only 2% of the decisions were TP-FN. Of these, 53% were reported on the first decision then omitted on the second; 47% were reported and classified correctly on the first decision, then misclassified on the second. The FN and the FP errors were equally spread among the different diagnostic categories and were equally spread over the various image processing functions - no processing function was associated with more FN or FP errors than any of the others.

FIGURE 1. Average number of times each image processing function was used for each diagnostic category.

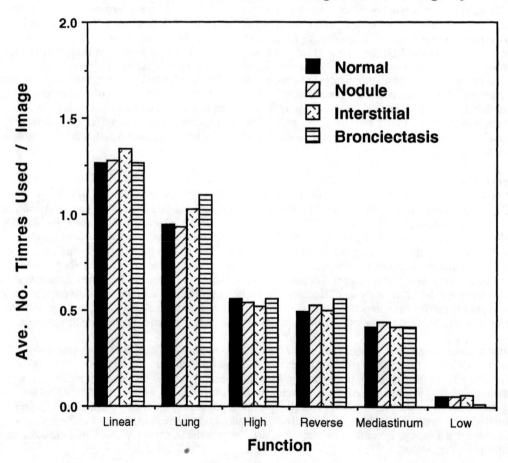

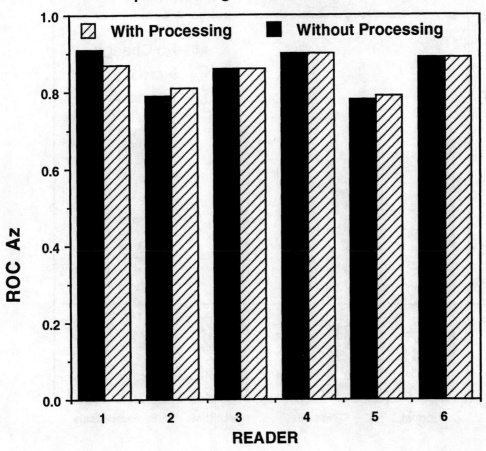

FIGURE 2. ROC Az values for the six radiologists for readings without and with use of image processing functions.

FIGURE 3. Percent decision confidence rating changes from without to with image processing use.

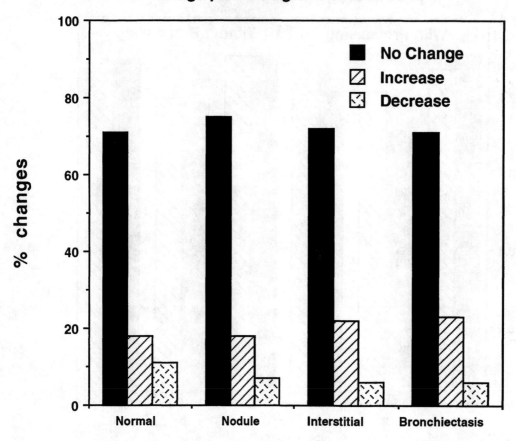

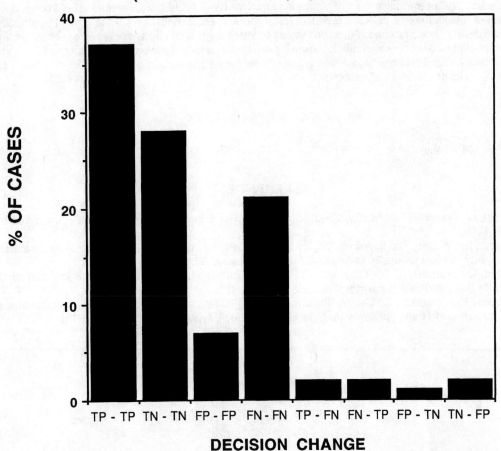

FIGURE 4. Percent of cases with various decision changes made without (first decision) and with (second decision) processing use.

4. CONCLUSIONS

The results of the present study indicate that, at least for the sample of cases and image processing functions used, image processing did not affect significantly diagnostic performance. The majority of cases did not change confidence (70% on average) or decision (93%) in any significant manner from without to with use of image processing. As noted previously, this result may only be generalizable to other CR chest images with the same disease entities processed in the same manner. However, the magnitude of the effect (or lack thereof in this case) is so great that the results are probably quite telling. If a radiologist does not see something on an image without the use of image processing, it is unlikely that global processing will reveal any missed abnormalities (only 2% in this study). It seems more likely that image processing has the effect of possibly increasing decision confidence once an abnormality is detected without image processing. In our study, decision confidence increased about 20% of the time after image processing use. It also decreased by about 10% on average, but the rate of confidence increase is about twice that of confidence decrease. These results suggest that radiologists might want to tend to be conservative in their use of image processing and that its real utility may be for enhancing the perception and clarification of suspicious areas detected prior to use of image processing.

The patterns of image processing use were also quite interesting. In general each radiologist quickly fell into a pattern of using (for the most part) only one or two processing functions. Overall the radiologists preferred to use the high-pass and the lung functions, which generally made the images appear sharper and slightly darker. No relationship was found between frequency of use of particular processing functions and specific disease categories. The radiologists preferred certain settings in general and did not alter the use of functions depending on what was in the image. This type of finding might change if different types of images (e.g., chest vs mammography) were considered. Similar studies tracking the use of processing functions for different disease entities should be conducted for other types of images to see if the same pattern of results occurs. These results have some general implications for workstation design. Image processing functions should be tested for general effectiveness and use before being implemented on clinical workstations. Radiologists using workstations should use processing functions on a variety of images and disease entities in order to see how image content for particular cases is affected with processing (e.g., learn what tends to lead to false-positive reports).

5. ACKNOWLEDGMENTS

This work was supported in part by Toshiba Medical Systems, Tokyo, Japan.

6. REFERENCES

1. H.K. Kundel, G. Revesz, H.M. Stauffer, "Evaluation of a television image processing system", *Invest Radiol* **3**, pp.44- 50, 1968.
2. S. Kheddache, L. Denbratt, J.A. Engelhed, "Digital chest radiography - optimizing image processing parameters for the visibility of chest lesions and anatomy", *Europ J of Radiol* **22**, pp. 241-245, 1996.
3. C.A. Britton, O.F. Gabriele, T.S. Chang, J.D. Towers, D.A. Rubin, W.F. Good, D. Gur, "Subjective quality assessment of computed radiography hand images", *J of Digital Imaging* **9**, pp. 21-24, 1996.
4. D.D. Dorfman, K.S. Berbaum, C.E. Metz, "Receiver operating characteristic rating analysis : generalization to the population of readers and patients with the jackknife method", *Invest Radiol* **27**, pp. 723-731, 1992.

Further author information

E.K. (correspondence): Email: krupinski@radiology.arizona.edu; Telephone: 520-626-4498; Fax: 520-626-4376

Influence of Monitor Luminance and Tone Scale on Observer Detection Performance

Elizabeth Krupinski[a], Hans Roehrig[a],Toshihiko Furukawa[b] and Chuankun Tang[a]

[a]Department of Radiology, University of Arizona, Tucson, AZ 85724
[b]DataRay Corporation, Westminster, CO 80234

ABSTRACT

The goal of this study was to determine the influence of adjusting monitor display parameters such as brightness and tone scale on observer diagnostic performance in order to determine what display settings are best for radiographic soft copy image display. Six radiologists viewed a series of 50 pairs of mammograms (craniocaudal and mediolateral views, right or left breast) on CRT monitors in two conditions. The images contained either a single subtle mass, a single subtle cluster of microcalcifications, or no lesion. In the first condition, the characteristic curve (tone scale) of the monitor was studied. Two curves were tested, one which was related to human perception and one which was typical for an unmodified CRT (default). In the second condition, display luminance was manipulated. Readers had to report on the presence of microcalcification clusters or masses and had to report their decision confidence using a 6-level rating scale. Monitor brightness (luminance) and tone scale can influence diagnostic performance to some degree. Whether the magnitude of these differences is important clinically needs to be further studied.

Keywords : observer performance, contrast, brightness, monitor display

1. INTRODUCTION

Digital image acquisition and display technologies are seeing a rapid rise in development and use in radiology departments. Optimal display design and performance factors are not, however, completely understood for most reading tasks. There are numerous perceptual, learning and ergonomic factors that must be considered when transitioning from film to filmless radiographic reading. [1] Image brightness (monitor luminance) is one very important factor. Radiographic viewboxes for reading film are quite bright (a luminance of over 1000 ftL is recommended for mammography) compared to monitors. However, viewing images on a monitor is fundamentally different from viewing images on a viewbox - are the luminance requirements therefore different? Monitors with about 200 ftL luminance levels are available today, but cost and useful lifetime are important considerations when considering use of these monitors. Tone scale (the characteristic curve, comparable to gamma with film) is also very important. There is fairly good evidence that a perceptually linearized[2] display, which optimizes the display by taking into account what the capabilities of the human visual system are, is better than a non-perceptually linearized display. Basically, perceptual linearization produces a tone scale in which equal changes in driving levels yield changes in luminance that are perceptually equivalent for the whole luminance range.[3-5]

There are also many factors which affect the choice of an optimal display, above and beyond these basic display factors. In radiology, the type of image displayed, the type of lesion to be detected, and the overall diagnostic task, affect significantly what the optimal display characteristics should be. Therefore, it is necessary to study a wide variety of tasks and display conditions in order to optimize display monitors for general radiographic reading (e.g., the optimal display for mammography may be quite different from that for chest). In the end it may be that it is possible to design a general purpose display station that can be used for most types of radiographic reading situations. The study presented here is part of an on-going series of experiments designed to determine the influence of adjusting various display (e.g., luminance, tone scale) parameters on diagnostic performance. Perceived image quality and radiologists' preferences for various display parameters are also being evaluated. Quite often, radiographic images are rated as having only fair or poor image quality, but diagnostic accuracy is not affected.[6] Such things as radiologist preferences and comfort levels with displays must be taken into account when considering which displays to use in the clinical setting. If the radiologists do not like the display or if it takes to long to read the image from the display (regardless of whether or not it affects diagnostic accuracy), it is not likely that they will use it.

2. METHODS & MATERIALS

A series of 50 pairs of mammograms (craniocaudal and mediolateral views, right or left breast) was collected. Eighteen of the cases had a single subtle mass, eighteen had a single subtle cluster of microcalcifications, and fourteen were lesion free. Cases with masses or microcalcifications were all biopsy proven, and the lesion-free cases had confirmed lesion-free status for at least three years. The films were digitized using a Lumisys (Lumisys, Sunnyvale, CA) digitizer with a spot size of 80 microns and a contrast resolution of 12 bits. For the monitor studies the images were displayed on DataRay DR110 (DataRay Corp., Westminster, CO) monitors (See Table 1 for basic specifications). For the brightness study, two monitors were used - one with 140 ftL maximum luminance and the other with 80 ftL maximum luminance. The default tone scale was used for image presentation. The monitors were the same in all other respects (e.g., resolution) besides luminance. For the tone scale (characteristic curve) study, the images were displayed only on the 140 ftL monitor. Two tone scales were used (see Figure 1) : the first was the perceptually linearized Barten[7,8] scale, and the second was the default scale of the monitor (not perceptually linearized).

Table 1. Basic specifications for the DR110 DataRay monitors.

Display Type	Portrait Mode
CRT Size	21" FS
Deflection Angle	90 deg
Active Display Area	11.5" x 15.5"
Phosphor	P-45
Bulb Transmission	52%
Panel	92% and 62%
Resolution	1728 x 2304
Refresh Rate	70 Hz

Figure 1. Characteristic curves used in the tone scale and luminance studies.

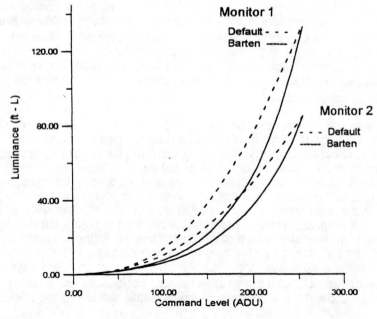

Figure 2. Light output vs anode peak current for the 140 ftL and 80 ftL DataRay DR110 monitors.

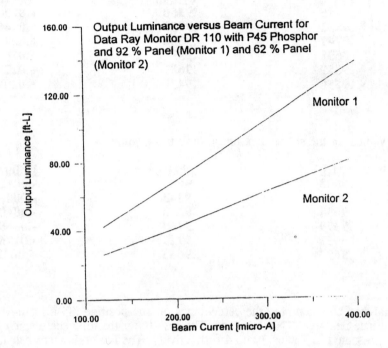

Six radiologists participated as readers in each study. For each study, a counterbalanced randomized image presentation order was used with at least two weeks between viewing sessions. Each session lasted about one hour. The pairs of images appeared on the monitor side-by-side (CC on the left, MLO on the right). No image processing (e.g., window/level) functions were available during the reading sessions. Readers could view images for as long as desired. Ambient room lights were turned off for this experiment. Viewing time was recorded (from the time the image appeared on the monitor until the reader hit the "next image" icon. For each case, the readers had to report their decisions in two parts. For the first decision readers had to decide if the case was lesion-free or if it contained a mass or microcalcification cluster. They then had to report their confidence in that decision using a six-level rating scale, where 1 = no lesion, definite and 6 = lesion present, definite. If a mass or microcalcification cluster was reported, readers had to indicate its position on an outline of the breast provided for that purpose. Readers could indicate more than one finding per case. Eye-position was recorded as the readers viewed the images, but those results are not presented here.

3. RESULTS

The confidence data were analyzed using Alternative Free Response Receiver Operating Characteristic (AFROC) analysis techniques since readers could indicate more than one finding per case. The area under the curve (A1) values for the six readers for the tone scale and luminance studies are presented in Tables 1 and 2 respectively. A t-test for paired observations was used to analyze the differences in conditions statistically. For the tone scale study, the Barten (mean = .9720, sd = .014) scale yielded significantly greater A1 values than did the default (mean = .9511, sd = .014) scale (t = 5.423, df = 5, p = .0029). For the luminance study, there was no statistically significant difference between the 140 ftL (mean = .9695, sd = .009) and the 80 ftL (mean = .9594, sd = .015) monitors (t = 1.685, df = 5, p = .1528).

Table 1. AFROC A1 values for the six readers in the tone scale study.

Reader	Barten	Default	Difference
1	.9746	.9550	+.0196
2	.9882	.9736	+.0146
3	.9747	.9366	+.0381
4	.9531	.9331	+.0200
5	.9859	.9631	+.0228
6	.9556	.9450	+.0106

Table 2. AFROC A1 values for the six readers in the luminance study.

Reader	80 ftL	140 ftL	Difference
1	.9603	.9655	-.0052
2	.9837	.9843	-.0006
3	.9498	.9538	-.0040
4	.9379	.9744	-.0365
5	.9551	.9727	-.0176
6	.9695	.9663	+.0032

The data were also analyzed by examining the percentages of true-positive (TP), false-negative (FN), false-positive (FP) and true-negative (TN) decisions. The results for the tone scale study and luminance studies are presented in Tables 3 and 4 respectively. The log odds were calculated for both studies and conditions compared using a chi-squared test. For the tone scale study the log odds were 3.55 for the Barten scale and 2.93 for the default scale. The difference was statistically significant (X^2 = 3.88, df = 1, p < .05). For the luminance study the log odds were 3.21 for 80 ftL and 3.53 for 140 ftL. The difference was not statistically significant (X^2 = .713, df = 1, p > .05).

Table 3. Percentages of TP, FN, FP and TN decisions across readers for the tone scale (characteristic curve) study.

Decision	Barten Scale	Default Scale
TP	88% (191/216)	84% (181/216)
FN	12% (25/216)	16% (35/216)
FP	5% (16/300)	6% (19/300)
TN	87% (73/84)	82% (69/84)

Table 4. Percentages of TP, FN, FP and TN decisions across readers for the luminance study.

Decision	80 ftL	140 ftL
TP	83% (179/216)	85% (183/216)
FN	17% (37/216)	15% (33/216)
FP	5% (14/300)	4% (12/300)
TN	86% (72/84)	88% (74/84)

Viewing time was also recorded and analyzed, and the results are presented in Table 5. For the tone scale study, viewing times with the Barten and Default scales did not differ significantly when tested with a t-test for paired observations (t = 1.02, df = 299, p = .3088). Viewing times with the Barten scale ranged from 11 sec to 98 sec and times for the Default scale ranged from 8 sec to 98 sec. For the luminance study, viewing time did differ significantly (t = 1.994, df = 299, p = .047) with viewing time lasting 3.71 sec longer on average on the 80 ftL monitor than on the 140 ftL monitor.

Viewing times ranged from 6 sec to 99 sec on the 80 ftL monitor, and from 10 sec to 99 sec on the 140 ftL monitor.

Table 5. Average viewing times (sec) and standard deviation (SD) values for the tone scale and luminance studies.

Condition	Mean	SD
Barten	49.53 sec	20.55
Default	47.85 sec	21.67
80 ftL	52.71 sec	24.08
140 ftL	48.99 sec	22.15

4. CONCLUSIONS

The data from the tone scale study support other studies that have found differences in tone scales favoring perceptually linearized scales over non-perceptually linearized scales. These results seem reasonable considering that the goal of a perceptually linearized display is to optimize the information presented to the observer in terms of what the observer is capable of processing perceptually. The use of perceptually linearized monitor displays is therefore recommended for viewing digitally displayed images. Although this study used only mammograms, it is likely that the results will be applicable to most radiographic imaging situations.

The data from the luminance study, however, suggest something rather unexpected. Overall, the readers did slightly better with the higher luminance (140 ftL) monitor. The overall difference in A1 performance and the differences in percentages of TP and FP responses were not statistically different, although A1 and the percentage of TPs were higher and the percentage of FPs lower with the higher luminance monitor. With a different set of images or different diagnostic task, the results might have been different. There is a trend for better performance with the higher luminance monitor, so it may be reasonable to suggest using the higher brightness monitor for clinical diagnoses. Again, much depends on the images and the task and further studies must be conducted to generalize these results to other clinical situations.

The viewing time data show some interesting results. The two tone scales were not associated with significantly different viewing times. The luminance study did, however, show significant differences in viewing time. Observers spent an average of about 4 sec longer per case on the 80 ftL monitor than on the 140 ftL monitor. Previous studies[9,10] comparing film with monitor reading have also found significant viewing time differences, with film taking much less time to read than images displayed on a monitor - often up to 60 sec less time. One possibility suggested for this difference in viewing time is the difference in luminance between images displayed on film vs a monitor. In this experiment, there was also a significant difference in display luminance, the only difference being that the two displays were both monitors instead of one monitor and one film display. The magnitude of the difference was not as great as that of film vs monitor, but there was a significant difference. The results support the hypothesis that display luminance can affect viewing time to some degree. The magnitude of the difference between film and monitor viewing may be due only in part to luminance factors. There are other factors to consider in that comparison - resolution and image size, for example. For the film vs monitor comparison, it was found[10] that dwell times on truly negative areas of images were significantly longer on the monitor than on film, while all other decisions did not differ significantly. The present study collected eye-position data as well, and that data will be analyzed to determine if the same pattern of dwell time results is present.

Further work in this area will involve using a third monitor which has a maximum luminance of 40 ftL as well as testing for differences in diagnostic performance as monitor resolution is changed. Other types of images (e.g., chest) will also be examined using the same experimental display parameters.

5. ACKNOWLEDGMENTS

This work was supported in part by the DataRay Corporation, Westminster, CO and Toshiba Medical Systems, Tokyo, Japan.

6. REFERENCES

1. J. Wang, S. Langer, "A brief review of human perception factors in digital displays for Picture Archiving and Communications Systems", *J Digital Imaging* **10**, pp 158-168, 1997.

2. S.M. Pizer, "Intensity mappings: linearization, image-based, user-controlled", *Proc SPIE* **271**, pp 21-27, 1981.

3. R.E. Johnston, J.B. Zimmerman, D.C. Rogers, S.M. Pizer, "Perceptual standardization," *Proc SPIE* **536**, pp. 44-49, 1985.

4. B.M. Hemminger, R.E. Johnston, J.P. Rolland, K.E. Muller, "Perceptual linearization of video display monitors for medical image presentation", *Proc SPIE* **2164**, pp. 222-241, 1994.

5. M.I. Sezan, K.L. Yip, S.J. Daly, "Uniform perceptual quantization: applications to digital radiography", *IEEE Trans Syst Man Cybern* **SMC-17**, pp. 622-634, 1987.

6. H. Roehrig, E.A. Krupinski, R. Hulett, "Reduction of patient exposure in pediatric radiology", *Academic Radiology* **4**, pp. 547-557, 1997.

7. H. Blume, E. Muka, "Presenting medical images on monochrome displays", *Information Display* **6**, pp. 14-17, 1995.

8. H. Blume, "The ACR/NEMA proposal for a grey-scale display function standard", *Proc SPIE* **2707**, pp. 344-360, 1996.

9. E.A. Krupinski, K. Maloney, S.C. Bessen, M.P. Capp, K. Graham, R. Hunt, P. Lund, T. Ovitt, J.R. Standen, "Receiver operating characteristic evaluation of computer display of adult portable chest radiographs", *Invest Radiol* **29**, pp. 141-146, 1994.

10. E.A. Krupinski, P.J. Lund, "Differences in time to interpretation for evaluation of bone radiographs with monitor and film viewing", *Acad Radiol* **4**, pp. 177-182, 1997.

Further author information

E.K. (correspondence): Email: krupinski@radiology.arizona.edu; Telephone: 520-626-4498; Fax: 520-626-4376

Robust and automatic adjustment of display window width and center for MR images

Shang-Hong Lai and Ming Fang

Siemens Corporate Research, 755 College Road East, Princeton, NJ 08540

ABSTRACT

The display of a 12-bit MR image on a common 8-bit computer monitor is usually achieved by linearly mapping the image values through a display window, which is determined by the width and center values. The adjustment of the display window for a variety of MR images involves considerable user interaction. In this paper, we present an advanced algorithm with the hierarchical neural network structure for robust and automatic adjustment of display window width and center for a wide range of MR images. This algorithm consists of a feature generator utilizing both histogram and spatial information computed from a MR image, a wavelet transform for compressing the feature vector, a competitive layer neural network for clustering MR images into different subclasses, a bi-modal linear estimator and an RBF (Radial Basis Function) network based estimator for each subclass, as well as a data fusion process to integrate estimates from both estimators of different subclasses to compute the final display parameters. Both estimators can adapt to new types of MR images simply by training them with those images, thus making the algorithm adaptive and extendable. This trainability makes also possible for advanced future developments such as adaptation of the display parameters to user's personal preference. While the RBF neural network based estimators perform very well for images similar to those in the training data set, the bi-modal linear estimators provide reasonable estimation for a wide range of images that may not be included in the training data set. The data fusion step makes the final estimation of the display parameters accurate for trained images and robust for the unknown images. The algorithm has been tested on a wide range of MR images and shown satisfactory results. Although the proposed algorithm is very comprehensive, its execution time is kept within a reasonable range.

Keywords: image perception, optimal display, magnetic resonance images, automatic windowing, brightness adjustment, contrast adjustment, neural networks, hierarchical neural networks, wavelet transform.

1.0 INTRODUCTION

Magnetic Resonance (MR) images have typically a data depth of 12 bits. For displaying a 12-bit MR image on a common 8-bit computer monitor, the image intensity range of the MR image needs to be re-mapped in general. One of the common re-mapping processes is the so-called windowing process. It maps the image intensity values linearly from [center-width/2, center+width/2] to [0, 255], where center and width are two display parameters to be adjusted. The image intensity values below (center-width/2) are mapped to zero, while they are set to 255 if greater than (center+width/2). Obviously, these two parameters can greatly influence the appearance of the image displayed. In other words, the brightness and the contrast of an image is determined by these two parameters. Inadequate adjustment of these parameters can lead to degradation of image quality and in severe cases to loss of valuable diagnostic information of the images.

Automatic adjustment of the above-mentioned two display parameters is in fact a very complicated problem because of the following reasons:

- The maximum and the minimum pixel intensity value are unstable quantities for the automatic adjustment of display parameters. They can be influenced strongly by many factors, such as spikes and background noise. This makes any simple algorithms using on the maximum and minimum of the image intensity unstable.

- The region of interest in the intensity domain may only occupy a small portion of the dynamic range of the image pixel values. It is therefore inadequate to map the entire dynamic range of an image to [0, 255].

- The spatial distribution of an image may also play an important role in the adjustment of the display window parameters. Different organs may have similar intensity distribution (histograms) but should be windowed differently.

This factor makes the use of other information sources beyond the histogram of MR images necessary. Unfortunately, all current algorithms known to us are based on histograms or its derivatives.

- It is also evident that the optimal display parameters also depend on the type of MR examinations. Different types of MR images may need to be viewed, and hence windowed differently. For example, 3D angiographic images, T1 or T2 weighted images, and inversion recovery images should be windowed very differently.

- It is also evident that the optimal display parameters also depend on the type of MR examinations. Different types of MR images may need to be viewed, and hence windowed differently. For example, 3D angiographic images, T1 or T2 weighted images, and inversion recovery images should be windowed very differently.

There have been some methods developed for automatic adjustment of display window's width and center values. The most simplest method is to determine the maximal and the minimal intensity values of each MR image, and then map them to [0, 255] in a linear fashion. This method does not work well in many cases because it dose not solve any problems mentioned above. In addition, the methods purely based on the histogram information to determine the display parameters can not provide satisfactory solutions for a wide range of MR images. We have found many cases in our testing data set that human operators have selected a very different setting of display parameters for some images with very similar histograms, but with different spatial distributions. To resolve this ambiguity for using histogram information only, we propose to utilize some spatial statistical information of the images in addition to the histogram information for the display window parameters determination in this report. The performance and robustness of our algorithm are greatly improved with the addition of spatial statistical information.

Wendt III [1] has proposed a method which determines at first the type of an MR image by reading the image header information, and then compute the display parameters depending on the type of the image. This provides a possibility to determine the actual field of view of the image to avoid pixels lying on the edge and outside of the field of view. It also ignores pixels that have values below a threshold depending on the type of image being processed. However, different rules must be set for different types and orientations of MR images in this method. This makes the algorithm somehow impractical, since the software may have to be re-programmed to reflect any new changes in the MR image acquiring process, such as the use of new coils or new pulse sequences. It is therefore very desirable to have some adaptation capability built-in so that the algorithm can adapt to these new coils or sequences without re-programming the software. An obvious possibility is to use neural networks which provide "learn by example" capability. By showing the new examples, the neural networks can be re-trained without re-programming.

There was a neural network based method developed for automatic adjustment of the display window by Ohhashi et al. [2]. A group of six features from the gray-level histogram of the MR images to be displayed is at first extracted. A back-propagation neural network is then trained to learn the relationship between these features and the desired output of the optimal display parameters set by human operators. Although this method has some advantages by utilizing a neural network, it is still a pure histogram based method, which has the potential problem for the images with different spatial distributions but very similar histograms. Furthermore, this method uses only one neural network to learn the relationship between histogram based features and the desired output of the optimal display parameters, which is very difficult to capture the very complex, sometimes even totally conflicting, relationship for the display window adjustment problem. There is an obvious need for using more networks for minimize the probability of conflicting situations.

In this paper, we present a comprehensive neural networks based algorithm for addressing all of the issues mentioned above. It is important to mention that our proposed algorithm can deal with the aforementioned problems reasonably well. Our algorithm uses both histogram and spatial statistical information of MR images for feature generation, followed by a hierarchical neural network based algorithm for estimating the display window width and center values. In addition, the framework of our algorithm is designed with easy extension for on-line adaptation capability, thus it can be developed as an adaptive system.

2.0 SYSTEM OVERVIEW

In this section, a system overview of our algorithm is outlined. The signal flow diagram of our algorithm is shown in Figure 1.

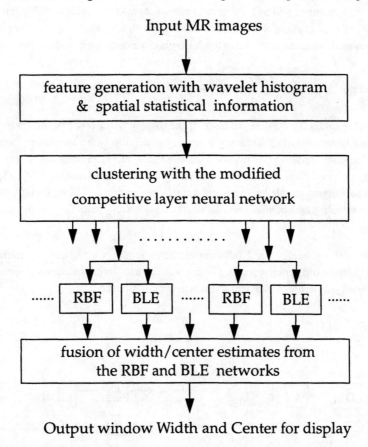

FIGURE 1. System overview of our neural network based algorithm, where RBF Radial Basis Function network and BLE represents the Bimodal Linear Estimation network.

Our algorithm uses both histogram and spatial intensity distributions of MR images for feature generation. This resolves in most cases the conflicting situations where the window display settings are very different although the histograms of the images are very similar. Since MR images have a data depth of 12 bits, the size of the image histogram could be large. It is therefore necessary to compress the histogram information into a much smaller size for efficient training of neural networks. We have implemented both wavelet transform and principal component analysis (PCA) methods for obtaining a compact representation of useful information from the MR images. Since our experiments did not show any significant performance difference between both methods and PCA is more computationally expensive, we decided to use the wavelet transform for our final implementation. For distinguishing different types of MR images, we have implemented a neural network based clustering algorithm, i.e. the competitive layer neural network, which clusters any input image into a certain number of clusters. We have used 120 different clusters in our current implementation for covering a wide range of different types of MR images. Furthermore, two totally different and independent estimation methods are used for each class for achieving good performance. Radial Bases Function (RBF) networks are used for providing accurate estimation for known (trained) MR image types, while bimodal linear networks provide robust and reasonable estimation for a wide range of images, that may not be included in the training data set. Finally, a data fusion step is implemented for making the algorithm accurate for trained images and robust for the unknown images.

In the subsequent sections, we will describe all components of our algorithm in more details.

3.0 FEATURE EXTRACTION

In this section, we discuss the representative features extracted from the input MR image used for the estimation of display window width and center, i.e. these features will be fed into the neural networks for window width/center estimation. The chosen features must be decisive for the adjustment of the display window width and center. The features used in our method consist of histogram features and spatial statistical features. In the following, we describe how these two different types of features are extracted from the image.

3.1 Histogram Features

Histogram information is very important for the determination of the display window width and center for an MR image. Several methods have been proposed previously to automatically adjust the window width and center for an image from its histogram. In our algorithm, the histogram features are extracted from the histogram of an image as follows. At first, the histogram is computed from the input image and a range of interest in the histogram is obtained from it. Within this range of interest, the histogram is first smoothed and then re-sampled using a pre-determined number of bins. Finally, we compute the wavelet transform of the new re-sampled histogram and take only the coefficients corresponding to the coarsest level as the histogram features.

We take the wavelet transform of the normalized and sub-sampled histogram vector and use the coefficients corresponding to the most representative bases to be the histogram features. For the wavelet transform, the wavelet bases in the coarsest level are chosen. In the following, we briefly describe the wavelet transform for completeness.

3.1.1 Wavelet Transform

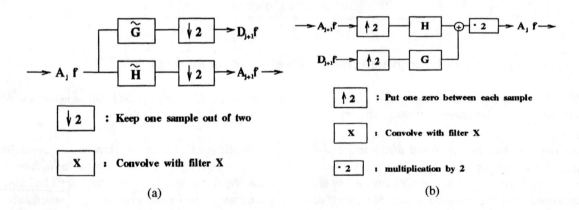

FIGURE 2. The implementation of the wavelet transform via the QMF structure [3] from one level to the next, (a) decomposition (b) reconstruction.

Wavelet transform has been used widely in the signal and image processing communities since it provides a powerful tool for multi-resolution analysis [3]. The wavelet decomposition and reconstruction can be efficiently achieved via a Quadrature Mirror Filters (QMF) implementation as shown in Figure 2. In this figure, $A_j f$ is the discrete approximation of the function f in the j-th resolutional subspace V_j, i.e. $A_j f$ contains the values of the inner products of the function f and the orthonormal basis functions in V_j, and $D_j f$ encodes the projection of the function f on the subspace W_j, that is a complement of V_j. The filters $\tilde{H}$ (in decomposition) and H (in reconstruction) are low-pass filters, while the filters $\tilde{G}$ (in decomposition) and G (in reconstruction) are high-pass filters. They are usually designed to be the FIR filters, which can be implemented via convolution operations. With an appropriate choice of a wavelet basis, we can find the associated finite impulse response (FIR) filters with very short length/span and the QMF filter implementation for the wavelet transform can be accomplished very efficiently.The QMF structure decomposes the space from one level to the next coarser level with each stage involving a low-pass and high-pass filtering. In our implementation, we use an orthogonal wavelet transform, which means the low-pass filter H is the same as $\tilde{H}$ and the high-pass filter G is the same as $\tilde{G}$. These filters are implemented by FIR filters of coefficients {-0.0761025, 0.3535534, 0.8593118, 0.3535534, -0.0761025} and coefficients {-0.0761025, -0.3535534, 0.8593118, -0.3535534, -0.0761025} for H and G, respectively.

3.1.2 Spatial Statistical Features

It is very difficult to achieve satisfactory window width and center adjustment capability similar to human experts purely based on the histogram information. This is because human experts adjust window width and center partially based on the types of MR images as well as the regions of interest in the images, which can not be recovered from the histogram information. This can be justified by the observation that sometimes two different images with very similar histograms can have very different window width and center values adjusted by human experts. Figure 3 depicts an example of two different MR images with very similar histograms but very different window width/center settings. By including the spatial statistical features into the complete feature vector, we can resolve this ambiguity problem due to only using insufficient histogram information. Therefore, we also use the spatial statistical features in addition to the above histogram features as the complete feature vector to be fed into the neural networks.

For the spatial statistical features, we first partition the whole image into 4-by-4 blocks. Then the mean and standard deviation of each individual block is used to form the spatial statistical features. We choose the feature vector which is the input to the neural networks to be the concatenation of the wavelet or KL histogram features discussed above and the spatial statistical features. This combined feature vector is denoted by V. By including the spatial statistical features into the whole feature vector, the window width/center estimation via our neural network training is greatly simplified. Furthermore, it also improves the robustness of our algorithm.

4.0 HIERARCHICAL NEURAL NETWORKS

We developed a new hierarchical neural network method for window width and center estimation. Our hierarchical neural networks contain a clustering network and estimation networks. The clustering network is used to classify the input feature vector into multiple classes which are most closest to it, instead of just one class. This concept is similar to the "soft" splits of data used in the hierarchical mixtures of experts [4]. In our clustering network, the competitive network is employed with the modification that a fixed number of closest classes are chosen, instead of just one. For each class, we have associated estimation networks to produce the window width and center estimation. Two types of estimation networks are employed here. One is the RBF (radial basis function) network and the other is the bi-modal linear network. The details of the aforementioned networks are described below.

4.1 Clustering Network

We modify the competitive layer network to classify the input feature vector V into multiple clusters instead of just one single cluster. There are totally N clusters in the competitive layer network. Each cluster is represented by a centroid u_i, where i is the cluster index. After the clustering, the input vector is assigned to m clusters which are closest to it. This can be accomplished by computing the distances between the input feature vector and all the centroids. Then the m clusters with the shortest distances to the input vector are the results of the clustering.

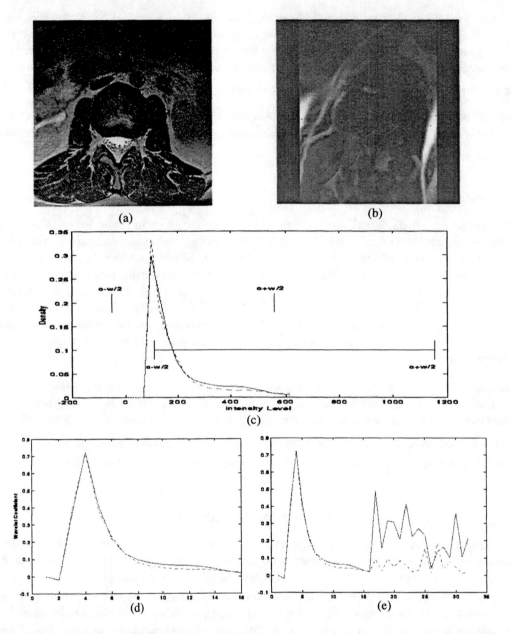

FIGURE 3. Two different MR images shown in (a) and (b) with very similar histograms but very different window width/center settings as shown in (c). Their wavelet histogram feature vectors are still very similar as shown in (d). With the inclusion of the spatial statistical features, the complete feature vectors become much more distinct as shown in (e).

4.2 Estimation Networks

After the input feature vector is classified into m clusters after the clustering network, it is fed into the corresponding estimation networks, which consist of RBF networks and bi-modal linear networks. The inclusion of the pre-clustering process has the advantage of reducing the complexity of the problem, i.e. it can divide a very complex function approximation problem in a big space to a number of simpler function approximation problems in smaller spaces. Each simpler function approximation problem is tackled by the RBF network as well as the bi-modal linear network separately. A brief description of these networks is given as follows.

4.2.1 RBF Networks

The input vector to the radial basis function (RBF) networks [5] is the same as the input vector to the competitive layer clustering network, i.e. the feature vector v discussed above. The output are the estimated window width $\hat{w}_i$ and center $\hat{c}_i$, where the subscript i denotes the index of the RBF network. The structure for an individual RBF network is shown below.

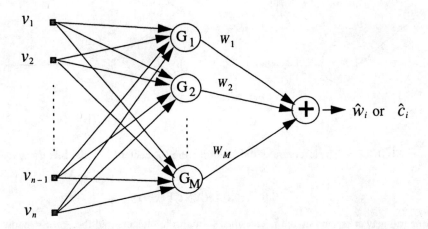

FIGURE 4. Structure of a RBF network for function approximation.

The RBF network has one hidden layer, which consists of M nodes in Figure 4. Each node is represented by a centroid x_j, where the subscript j denotes index of the node. The input to each node is the feature vector v. The output of each node is a radial basis function of the distance between the input feature vector and the associated centroid, i.e. $G(v;x_j)$. Here we use the multivariate Gaussian function as the radial basis function, thus we have

$$G(v;x_j) = e^{-\frac{\|v - x_j\|^2}{\sigma^2}}$$

where the symbol $\| \ \|$ stands for the Euclidean norm and σ is the spatial constant. The contribution of each node to the estimate is given by the weight W_j. The centroids and the weights are obtained through the RBF network training from a large image data set with the associated window width and center values adjusted by human experts. The total number of nodes used in each RBF network depends on the complexity of the training data points classified into this cluster. This is usually determined during the training process.

4.2.2 Bi-modal Linear Networks

The basic idea behind the use of the bi-modal linear networks here is the observation that the distribution of the ratios between the window width or center values adjusted by human experts and the corresponding window width or center reference values discussed above in each cluster can be roughly approximated by a mixture of two Gaussian functions. The bi-modal linear networks for each cluster are designed to produce two window width or center estimates corresponding to the means of the two Gaussian distributions. One of these two estimates is a robust indicator to the goodness of the estimates obtained by the RBF networks. We will use the outputs of the bi-modal linear networks to define confidence measures for the estimates from the

RBF networks and then combine these estimates based on the associated confidence measures to obtain the final window width and center estimates. The structure of the bi-modal linear network for each cluster is shown in Figure 5.

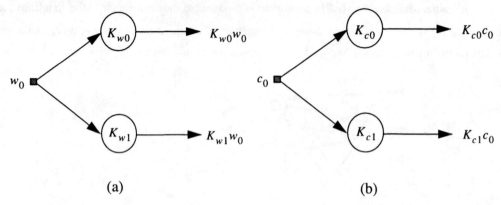

(a)   (b)

FIGURE 5. The structure of the (a) width and (b) center bi-modal linear networks.

5.0 INTELLIGENT FUSION

In our hierarchical neural networks, one image is classified to multiple clusters and there are window width and center estimates from the corresponding RBF networks and bi-modal linear networks for each selected cluster. It is important to intelligently combine the estimates obtained from these different networks, thus providing a robust and accurate estimation of the display window parameters. Although the input features and the network structures of the RBF network and bi-modal linear network are quite different, we use the same image data set and the same clustering results to train these networks. The window width and center estimates for a new image produced by these two different networks should be consistent with each other if the input image is similar to one of the images in the training data set.

The philosophy of fusing all different estimates to obtain the final window width and center estimate is to take the weighted average of the estimates from the RBF networks with each weight determined by the degree of consistency between the estimate from the RBF network and the corresponding estimate from the bi-modal network for the same cluster. The consistency measure is defined as the relative distance between the estimates from the two different networks in the same cluster. This is because the RBF network can give more accurate estimation when the input image is correctly classified into the cluster, while the estimates produced by the bi-modal linear network are more rough but more robust. Therefore, the estimates from the bi-modal linear networks are used as the reference values for the RBF network estimation.

6.0 NETWORK TRAINING

Our hierarchical neural networks consist of the competitive layer clustering networks, RBF estimation networks and bi-modal linear estimation networks. The training of these networks require a large set of various MR images with the window width and center values adjusted by the human experts to be the training data. The feature vectors are extracted from the MR images to be the input vectors to the neural networks, and the window width and center values are normalized to be the anticipated outputs for the estimation networks. The training for these different networks used in our implementation are basically accomplished by standard training algorithms in neural networks. We briefly discuss them in this section.

The competitive layer clustering networks is trained via an unsupervised Kohonen learning rule [6]. Since it is an unsupervised training, we only need to use the input feature vectors for the training. After the training, we obtain N vectors u_1, u_2, ..., u_N, which are the centers of the clusters. Note that the training of the clustering networks has to be completed before the training of the estimation networks for each cluster.

For the training of the RBF and bi-modal linear estimation networks, we need not only the computed input feature vectors but also the normalized window width and center values as the anticipated outputs of the networks. In addition, the training of these estimation networks requires clustering results. For the RBF networks in each cluster, the training algorithm is to minimize the maximum of the relative errors between the anticipated output and the network output by incrementally adding nodes into the networks. The training of the bi-modal linear networks is based on roughly classifying the data into two groups for each cluster, then the weight for each group can be easily computed by averaging the ratios of the anticipated outputs to the corresponding inputs.

7.0 EXPERIMENTAL RESULTS

In our implementation, we used 2436 MR images of various types and studies with their window width and center values adjusted by human experts for the training of the neural networks. For the testing of our algorithm, we used four hundred and sixty various MR images of diverse types as the testing data set and took the corresponding window width and center values adjusted by human experts as the ground truth values. Note that the testing MR images along with their window width and center settings could be very different from those in the training data set. center when the testing and training data sets are the same. In our implementation, the total number of clusters N is empirically set to 120, and the total number of assigned clusters for each input image m is chosen to be 5.

TABLE 1. Summary of the training results on 2436 MR images for our hierarchical neural network method. Note that a comprised setting for the training is used to avoid the over-training problem and provide good generalization capability.

Error Bound	Percentage of Width Estimates	Percentage of Center Estimates
20%	93.86%	93.97%
30%	97.95%	98.52%
40%	98.93%	99.59%
50%	99.26%	99.71%

Note that we can achieve perfect training results by keep increasing the total number of clusters in our hierarchical networks or the nodes in the RBF networks. However, it may fall into the over-training problem, thus reducing its generalization power. To avoid this over-training problem, we chose a compromised setting that can train the networks reasonably well but still provides good generalization capability to our networks. Table 1 depicts the training results of our networks for the percentages of the width and center estimates of the training data set with the relative error below 20%, 30%, 40% and 50%. The average relative errors are 7.06% for the width estimation and 6.97% for the center estimation. The average absolute errors are 45.7 and 76.4 for the center and width estimates, respectively. Note that the relative error is more useful than the absolute error in the accuracy assessment of the window width/center adjustment problem, since the ranges of the intensity values (or window width/ center values) for MR images can be very different from images to images. The absolute error is just given for reference. These trained networks will be used to test the 460 diverse MR images in the testing data set, which is exclusive from the training data set. The human adjusted window width and center values for these images are used as the ground truth for assessing the accuracy of our hierarchical neural network estimation.

TABLE 2. Summary of the results of the experiment on the testing data set containing 460 diverse MR images, which are completely different from those in the training data set, by using our hierarchical neural network method.

Error Bound	Percentage of Width Estimates	Percentage of Center Estimates
20%	63.48%	78.59%
30%	84.13%	88.04%
40%	93.26%	94.57%
50%	96.74%	96.74%

The generalization power of our hierarchical neural networks (with the training results given in Table 1) is tested on a totally different data set containing 460 diverse MR images. The human adjusted window width and center values for these images are used as the ground truth for assessing the accuracy of our hierarchical neural network estimation. The results of applying our algorithm on this testing data set are reported in Table 2. The average relative errors for the center and width estimates are 15.07% and 18.01%, respectively. In general, there is no significant difference between the image displayed with the window width and center values adjusted by human experts and by our neural network method when the relative errors are within 20% - 30%. Based on Table 2, we can conclude that our hierarchical neural network algorithm can give satisfactory window width and center estimation for approximately 85% diverse MR images that have not been trained to our networks.

Since the there are almost no noticeable differences between the displays of the images using the display window parameters provided by our algorithm and by human experts when the estimation errors are within 20%-30%, we only depict some MR images with the largest estimation errors from our hierarchical neural network method to show the robustness of our algorithm in figure 6. These MR images are shown with the window width and center values adjusted by human experts and by our neural network algorithm. For these images, our algorithm gives more than 50% errors either in window width or center estimates. Note that our algorithm fails to provide the window width/center estimates within 50% errors for only less than 5% of the images in the testing data set. *The displays of the images with the worst estimation results depicted in figure 6 show that the estimates provided by our algorithm with largest relative deviations from the settings by human experts are still reasonable, although they may not be the optimal settings for each individual.*

8.0 CONCLUSIONS

In conclusion, we proposed a robust and accurate display window width/center estimation algorithm for MR images based on the hierarchical neural networks. The wavelet histogram features and the spatial statistical features are extracted from the images and used as the input feature vector to the neural networks. Our hierarchical neural networks consist of a competitive layer neural network for clustering, 240 RBF networks and 240 bi-modal linear networks for estimation. The clustering network classifies an image into multiple clusters. Then the estimates from the associated estimation networks of these clusters are combined to provide the final estimation. The fusion of these estimates is accomplished by weighted averaging the estimates from the RBF networks with the weight determined by a consistency measure between the two estimates from the RBF network and bi-modal network in the same cluster. Satisfactory estimation results have been obtained from our experiments.

9.0 ACKNOWLEDGEMENTS

The authors would like to thank Siemens MED MR for providing the financial support, helpful suggestions as well as necessary MR image data for this work.

10.0 REFERENCES

1. R. E. Wendt III, "Automatic adjustment of contrast and brightness of magnetic resonance images", Journal of Digital Imaging, Vol. 7, No. 2, pp. 95-97, 1994.

2. A. Ohhashi, S. Yamada, K. Haruki, H. Hatano, Y. Fujii, K. Yamaguchi and H. Ogata, "Automatic adjustment of display window for MR images using a neural network", Proceeding of SPIE, Vol. 1444, Image Capture, Formatting and Display, pp. 63-74, 1991.

3. S. G. Mallat, "A theory of multiresolution signal decomposition", IEEE Trans. Pattern Anal. Machine Intell., Vol. 11, No. 7, pp. 647-693, 1989.

4. M. I. Jordan and R. A. Jacobs, "Hierarchical mixtures of experts and the EM algorithm", MIT A.I. Memo, No. 1440, 1993.

5. S. Haykin, *Neural Networks*, Macmillan College Pub., New York, 1994.

6. T. Kohonen, *Self-Organization and Associative Memory*, 2nd Ed., Springer-Verlag, Berlin, 1987.

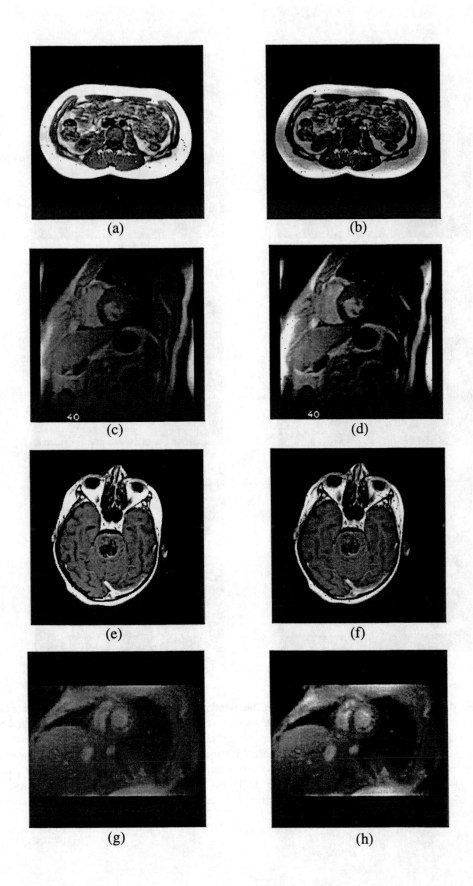

(a)

(b)

(c)

(d)

(e)

(f)

(g)

(h)

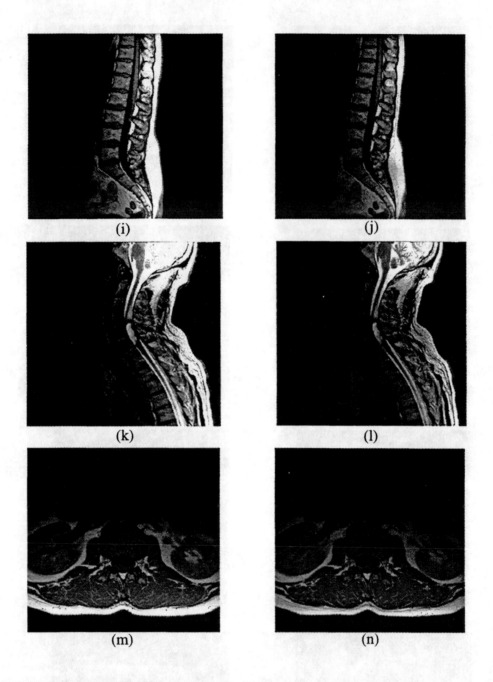

FIGURE 6. The MR images with the largest errors in the window width/center estimation from our neural network algorithm. These images are shown with the window width and center values adjusted by human experts and by our neural network algorithm shown in the left and right columns, respectively. For these images among the worst estimation results, the displays with the window width/center values provided by our algorithm are still reasonable as shown in the figure, although they may not be the optimal settings. The relative differences between the above two settings for the pairs (a)-(b), (c)-(d), (e)-(f), (g)-(h), (i)-(j), (k)-(l) and (m)-(n) are 55%(center) and 57%(width), 31%(center) and 50%(width), 39%(center) and 69%(width), 32%(center) and 52%(width), 74%(center) and 85%(width), 59%(center) and 69%(width), 58%(center) and 63%(width), respectively.

Effect of the reconstruction technique on the quality of digital mosaic mammograms

V. Swarnakar, M. Jeong, S. Smith and H. Kim D. Wobschall.

Sensor Plus, Amherst, NY, 14226

Digital mosaic imaging techniques provide a cost effective means to acquiring high resolution images. Constrained mosaic imaging techniques make use of special purpose fiducial patterns in order to define a-priori the relation between images on each tile. This "inter-tile" relation is applied to any images acquired subsequently. A simulation study was carried out where a model of the digital mosaic imager was used. By doing so, it was possible to compare the original data to that reconstructed using different techniques. The effects of these techniques on the quality of the final digital mosaic image were investigated. The techniques were applied towards reconstructing mammogram images. In order to evaluate performance of the approach, a set of features of interest were selected to measure image quality. Features that are important to visual perception include micro-calcifications and other fine details on the image, as per a radiologist's suggestion. Features important to the computerized diagnostic software include, edge maps and other common features used in existing computerized mammogram analysis approaches. Results of this experimental study provide a better understanding of how mosaic reconstruction approaches affect the quality of the final image. The study is also helpful in defining the role that features of interest, be it from a visual perception or computer software point of view, play towards selecting the image reconstruction scheme better suited for digital mosaic mammography. [Acknowledg]

Keywords: Digital Mammography, Image Quality, Mosaic Image Reconstruction

1. INTRODUCTION

Some of the desired features for digital mammography systems are cost, high resolution and large field of acquisition. Digital X-ray images to sever as successful replacement for film must be aimed at satisfying these requirements. Two basic approaches are currently under investigation for digital mammography. The most commonly employed of the two is the one in which conventional mammograms are digitized. The second approach is a digital imaging approach, wherein the mammogram is acquired digitally, via the use of CCD sensors[2][3]. In this approach CCD sensors are employed to observe an "imprint" of the x-ray mammogram on a surface such as Amorphous Selenium [1].

Existing approaches for digital mosaic imaging can be divided into two groups: (1) constrained mosaic imaging (2) un-constrained mosaic imaging. In constrained imaging approaches, a-priori information such as location of custom designed fiducial markers or precise knowledge of the imaging geometry is required. Un-constrained imaging approaches use only the information available within each imaging tile. Both approaches introduce artifacts in the final reconstructed image. Quality of the final mosaic image depends on the approach chosen. For mammography applications, it is imperative that the approach used introduces no artifacts that may hinder the diagnostic value of the final image. Artifacts can be perceived visually or detected by computerized diagnosis schemes. Images with no visually perceptible artifacts may contain distortions that deteriorate performance of a computerized diagnostic software. Conversely, images suitable

---

[Acknowledg]:This work was supported through an Army Breast Cancer Research grant.

for computerized analysis may not have good visual diagnostic quality. Therefore it is important to define parameters and thresholds by which the quality of the final mosaic image can remain valuable to both visual assessment and computerized diagnosis.

In this work the constrained mosaic imaging approach is investigated. Custom designed calibration screens were used to achieve a high degree of accuracy in the reconstruction. The next section presents a brief overview of the digital mosaic imager. Section 3 contains a description of the mammogram selection process. Three types of reconstruction techniques were implemented. Each technique was applied towards mosaic image reconstruction and qualitative analysis results are presented in section 4. Results obtained by analyzing a set of mammograms using the different reconstruction techniques are presented.

2. MOSAIC IMAGING

An illustration of the mosaic imaging procedure is shown in Figure 1. In this example four CCD sensors are placed in a matrix type architecture where adjacent sensors 'observe' an overlapping field of the image plane. The digital mosaic image is reconstructed by correcting any geometric distortions introduced by the optical components and subsequently stitching the corrected images. It should be noted that as there is overlap between the fields of view of each CCD sensor, the stitching step is required to eliminate redundancy. As this work is based upon using constrained mosaic imaging approach, a calibration screen is employed to aid the correction of distortions. Subsequent stitching of images is also facilitated due the use of the calibration screen. It can be noticed, as the results section will illustrate, that the correction scheme plays a critical role in the final quality of the mosaic image.

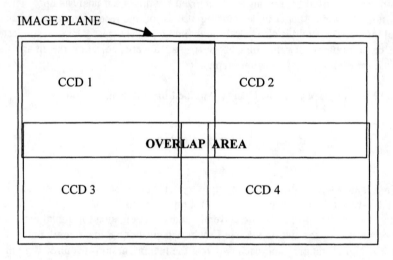

Figure 1. Model for the mosaic imager.

2.1 Distortion Correction

Several approaches have been proposed to correct distortions introduced by optical components of an imaging system[4]. One family of such approaches is based upon the use of a calibration pattern containing fiducial markers. The geometric relationship between the fiducial markers is known a-priori. Therefore an inverse transformation can be computed to relate pixel coordinates of the fiducials in the acquired image to the original pattern. Another approach is to develop a mathematical model of the optical components and use this model to recover the original pattern. This later approach has limitations when the underlying optical components can undergo changes as a function of time. Furthermore in the case of mosaic imaging, several such components are used and modeling each component individually can be an expensive task. In this work the former approach is used.

Throughout the following, I represents an image, the subscript index k represents the kth CCD and the superscript letters are r : for reference image (in the image plane), d : for digitized image and c: for corrected image. Let I_k^r be defined as a part of the original image, corresponding to the image area within the field of view of the kth CCD in the image plane. Also let I_k^d represent I_k^r once it is digitized by the CCD imager. In earlier work an approach based upon using piece-wise linear approximation was described in detail[2]. In this work two additional approaches are used. A new calibration pattern has been developed to aid in improving the accuracy of the distortion correction stage. Let (x_i^d, y_i^d) be the coordinates of a fiducial marker in the digitized image. These markers can be mapped on the reference pattern I_k^r using the a-priori known geometric relation between the fiducials. Let (x_i^r, y_i^r) be the coordinates of the associated fiducial in the reference pattern I_k^r. Given a set of such fiducials with their coordinates in the digitzed image and their associated fiducials with coordinate values as mapped onto the reference image, a pair of transformations T_x and T_y can be defined such that

$$x_i^r = T_x(x_i^d) \ and \ y_i^r = T_y(y_i^d).$$
(1)

Where the functions T_x and T_y model the distortion introduced by the imager. In this work *Bilinear* interpolation and *Spline* interpolation are used to model the distortion functions T_x and T_y. Using the interpolating functions the coordinates of any pixel in the digitized image I_k^d can be associated to a point on the reference pattern. The images I_k^c obtained by applying the functions T_x and T_y are an approximation to the original calibration pattern I_k^r. In Figure 2. the acquired images of the calibration pattern used in this work are shown. The intersection points of each line and the lines themselves are considered fiducials. The geometry of the pattern is well defined so that it is fairly straight forward to identify those sections that are overlapping in each image. Figure 3. shows the reconstructed image after each of the small images of Figure 2 have been corrected using spline interpolation approach and subsequently stitched as described below.

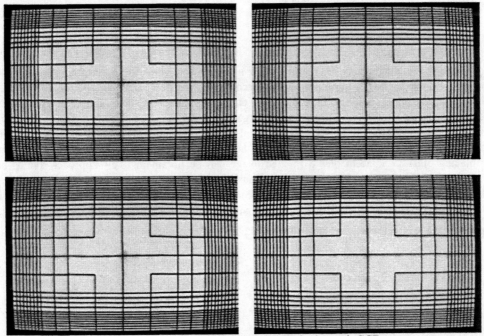

Figure 2. Images of the calibration pattern as acquire by each CCD sensor.

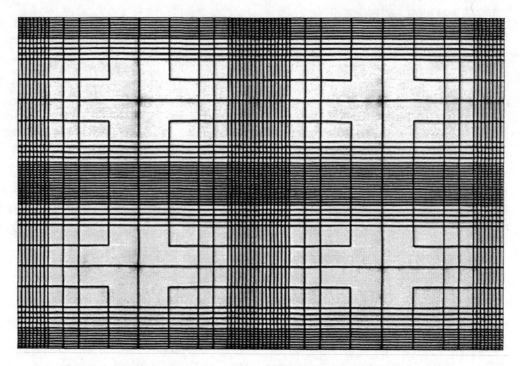

Figure 3. Mosaic image reconstructed using the spline interpolation algorithm.

It should be noted that the piece-wise linear approach uses only four fiducials during a step, while the bilinear and spline approaches are applicable to any number of fiducials. Thereby the piece-wise linear approach is a localized correction scheme while the bilinear and spline approaches are global correction schemes.

2.2 Stitching

Once the digitized images have been corrected the next step is to stitch these to form a mosaic. One way of stitching is to use an energy minimization approach to find the best matching coordinates of two images. This approach requires additional interpolation of the pixel values. This methodology is difficult to be used effectively when the underlying image has undergone a non-linear distortion. An alternative is to use the geometry of the calibration pattern. It is fairly simple to identify that section of an image that belongs to the overlap area. Therefore by extracting the part of the corrected image that does not fall in the overlap area and placing these in adjacent tiles a stitched image can be obtained. This approach avoids additional interpolation of the corrected image. However if adjacent tile images include effects of large angle rotation, this simplified stitching cannot be carried out accurately. In this work this later approach is chosen under the assumption that there are no large angle rotations in the digitized images. Then an approximation to the original image I^0 on the image plane is given by:

$$I^O = \mathbf{U}(I_k^c) \tag{2}$$

3. MAMMOGRAM SELECTION

Once a reconstructed image is available the next step is to evaluate the quality of the reconstruction. This issue is directly related to the case when acquiring images of mammograms. In practice though, the original image is unknown and only the reconstructed image is available. In order to properly study the effects of the reconstruction technique, the original image is also required. In this work a series of mammograms were digitally distorted and then stitched in order to carry out qualitative analysis. This process is described in the Section 4.

Quality of the reconstructed images can evaluated numerically and visually. Furthermore this evaluation can be carried out by observing the entire image, or some selected features of interest from the image. A variety of features of interest can be chosen from a mammogram. After consulting with the radiological experts involved it was decided that for this work three types of features would be investigated:

- Circumscribed mass
- Spiculated mass
- Micro-calcification.

A set of mammograms were selected from the Mammographic Image Analysis Society database. This is a publicly available database[7]. The images chosen here were all of size 1024x1024 and with a 200 micrometers pixel size resolution. The types of masses investigated are listed in the table below.

Feature	Tissue Type	Radius
Circumscribed Mass	Fatty	29 pixels
Spiculated Mass	Fatty Glandular	53 pixels
Microcalcification-A.	Dense	25 pixels
Microcalcification-B.	Dense	8 pixels

Table I. Types of features of interest from the mammograms.

The next section contains analysis results for three mammograms. The radius of the area surrounding each feature of interest in these mammograms is also listed in the table above. Areas with micro-calcification were from the same image.

4. RESULTS

Results presented here simulate a system where four CCD sensors are used to create the digital mosaic. By simulation it is understood that a mathematical model of the individual imaging components was employed instead of building the system.

The overlap area of four tiles is where the most severe distortions are expected to occur. In order to evaluate the quality of the reconstructed features, each mammogram was translated and placed in a larger image such that the feature of interest falls on the overlap region of all four tiles. So the mammograms are centered in a larger image using the center coordinates of the feature of interest as the center point of the larger image. The size of the large image is 1497x969 pixels and it is the same as that of the calibration pattern. Next four overlapping subsections of size 768x512 are extracted from the large image. Note that the resolution of the CCD's used in the imager is also 768x512 pixels. This will enable the application of the imager's distortion function to the mammogram images. It should be noted that each sub-image undergoes a slightly different transformation. The distortion function used was based upon a Barrel Distortion model. As it can be observed from the images in Figure 2 and 3 this function is suitable to approximate the imager optics. Once each sub-image is distorted using the distortion function the three correction schemes, Piece-wise linear approximation, Bilinear interpolation and Spline interpolation were applied to correct each sub-image. Sections from the corrected sub-images that do not belong to the overlap area are extracted and then placed together to form the reconstructed mosaic. The sections that do not fall in the overlap area were of size 729x485 pixels. Consequently the reconstructed image is the same size as the initial large mammogram image.

4.1 Quantitative analysis

One way of examining the reconstruction quality is to compute numerical measures of disparity between the original image and the reconstructed image. In this work, three measures, namely the Mean Absolute Error (MAE), the Mean Squared Error (MSE) and the Cross Correlation coefficient were used[5]. Given two images I_1 and I_2 of some size NxM the above quantities can be defined below.

Mean Absolue Error (MAE) :

$$MAE(I_1, I_2) = 1/N * M \sum_{i,j} |I_1(i,j) - I_2(i,j)| \tag{3}$$

Mean Square Error (MSE):

$$MSE(I_1, I_2) = 1/N * M \sum_{i,j} (I_1(i,j) - I_2(i,j)|)^2 \tag{4}$$

Cross Correlation Coefficient:

$$\rho = \frac{\sigma_{12}}{\sigma_1 \sigma_2} \tag{5}$$

Where in equation (5) above, σ_1, σ_2 are the variances of the images I_1 and I_2 and σ_{12} is the joint variance of these images. The correlation coefficient measures the disparity in between the two images globally. Whereas the MAE and MSE estimators provide an average estimate of the local behavior of the two images. Initially all these measures were computed using the entire large mammogram image. The results are shown in Table II. below. In general it was observed that the Bilinear interpolation based method performed better than the other two.

Mean Absolute Error			
Feature	Piece-wise Linear	Bilinear	Spline
Circumscribed Mass	1.19	0.78	1.09
Spiculated Mass	0.72	0.49	0.70
Microcalcification-A.	0.67	0.43	0.55

Mean Squared Error			
Feature	Piece-wise Linear	Bilinear	Spline
Circumscribed Mass	31.72	27.76	17.15
Spiculated Mass	35.09	26.88	29.13
Microcalcification-A.	26.25	19.22	15.01

Cross Correlation Coefficient			
Feature	Piece-wise Linear	Bilinear	Spline
Circumscribed Mass	0.9969	0.9973	0.9974
Spiculated Mass	0.9945	0.9958	0.9954
Microcalcification-A.	0.9956	0.9968	0.9975

Table II. Quantitative results computed on the entire reconstructed image.

Next these disparity measures were applied to sub-sections of the reconstructed image where the features of interest were located. Sections of size 128x128 were extracted from the central part of the reconstructed image. This is the region where the four tiles overlap and where the maximum distortion is expected to occur. Results obtained for these images are shown in the table below. From these tables it can be observed that again bilinear interpolation provided the best and most consistent results.

Mean Absolute Error			
Feature	Piece-wise Linear	Bilinear	Spline
Circumscribed Mass	1.48	1.08	1.16
Spiculated Mass	1.44	1.09	1.55
Microcalcification-A.	1.33	1.05	1.11
Microcalcification-B.	1.36	1.19	1.97

Mean Squared Error			
Feature	Piece-wise Linear	Bilinear	Spline
Circumscribed Mass	4.70	2.58	2.97
Spiculated Mass	3.96	2.37	2.66
Microcalcification-A.	3.55	2.26	2.53
Microcalcification-B.	3.79	2.99	8.85

Cross Correlation Coefficient			
Feature	Piece-wise Linear	Bilinear	Spline
Circumscribed Mass	0.9989	0.9994	0.9993
Spiculated Mass	0.9957	0.9974	0.9971
Microcalcification-A.	0.9952	0.9969	0.9965
Microcalcification-B.	0.9923	0.9939	0.9821

Table III. Quantitative results computed regions with features of interest.

4.2 Visual Analysis

Visual assessment of the image quality is a subjective task. Nevertheless an experienced observer can successfully identify any anomalies introduced by the reconstruction procedure. Visual evaluation of the large images revealed that when observing these images with zoom factors of up-to four times, no significant distortions were noticed. In general, the Spline based approach provided the most "visually pleasing" results. Similar observation was made when visually observing the regions with features. In

Figures 3-A,B,C,D a series of images of the areas with features of interest are shown. These images were enhanced using the *un-sharp* filtering operation [6].

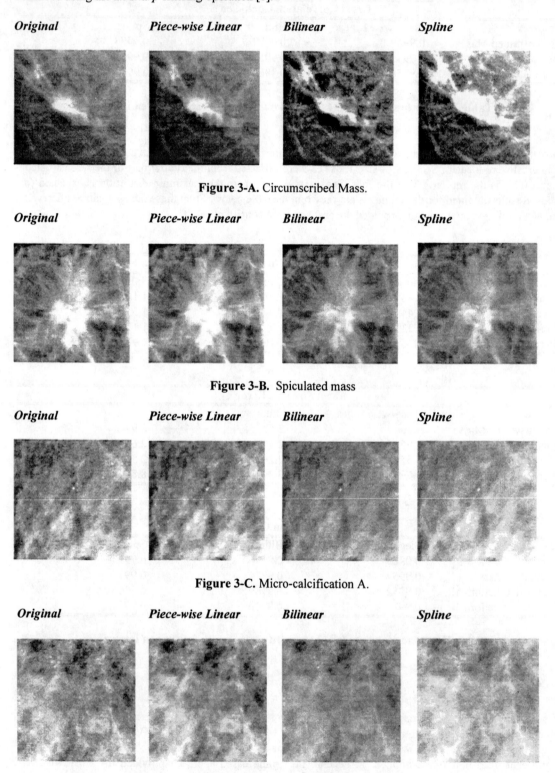

Original   *Piece-wise Linear*   *Bilinear*   *Spline*

Figure 3-A. Circumscribed Mass.

Original   *Piece-wise Linear*   *Bilinear*   *Spline*

Figure 3-B. Spiculated mass

Original   *Piece-wise Linear*   *Bilinear*   *Spline*

Figure 3-C. Micro-calcification A.

Original   *Piece-wise Linear*   *Bilinear*   *Spline*

Figure 3-D. Micro-calcification B.

As it can be observed the differences between each reconstruction scheme are better viewed under such a transformation. However, this operation is usually applied to images prior to using a computerized analysis algorithm. Therefore the effects of these differences will reflect in the performance of the computer algorithm. A simple edge enhancement and detection routine is applied to the filtered images. Results from this operation are shown in Figures 4-A,B,C and D.

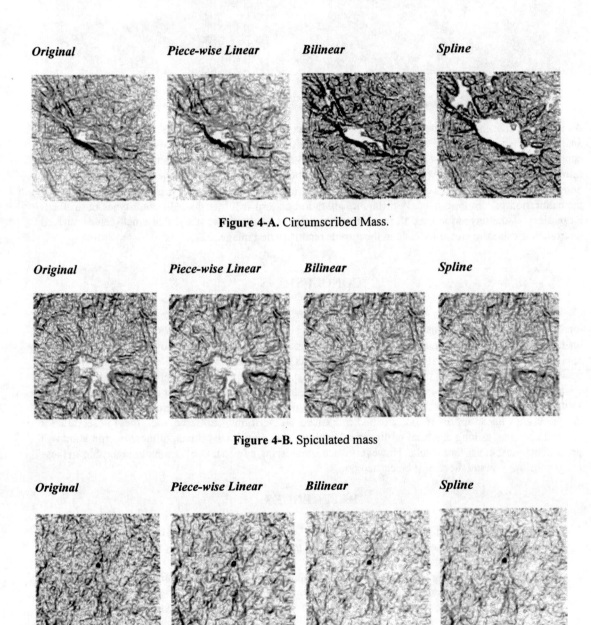

Original   *Piece-wise Linear*   *Bilinear*   *Spline*

Figure 4-A. Circumscribed Mass.

Original   *Piece-wise Linear*   *Bilinear*   *Spline*

Figure 4-B. Spiculated mass

Original   *Piece-wise Linear*   *Bilinear*   *Spline*

Figure 4-C. Micro-calcification A.

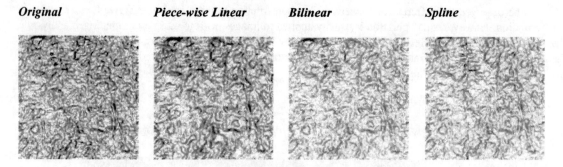

| *Original* | *Piece-wise Linear* | *Bilinear* | *Spline* |

Figure 4-D. Micro-calcification B.

As it is clear that the computer algorithm's performance is significantly different for each of the images analyzed. When observing the smaller feature images, visually it can be argued that the spline interpolation approach provided the most accurate results. However, the edge enhancement algorithm was least influenced when the images were reconstructed using the piece-wise linear scheme. Some artifacts can be noticed in the piece-wise linear approach. It can also be assumed that the artifacts introduced are related to the calibration pattern employed. A different calibration pattern will introduce different types of artifacts. Regardless of the technique used to reconstruct the images, it should be noted that small details such as micro-calcifications were still visible in the mosaic reconstructed image.

CONCLUSIONS

The primary objective of this work was to present the effect that different reconstruction schemes have on the quality of the digital mosaic mammograms. Using the constrained mosaic imaging approach three different reconstruction schemes were investigated. Numerical and visual evaluation of the effects of these approaches were presented. Numerical evaluation results can support that the bilinear interpolation scheme provides the most consistent results regardless of the type of features present in the mammogram. Visual evaluation on the other hand indicated that spline reconstruction provides the most accurate reconstruction. Lastly, when using a simple computer algorithm on regions with features of interest it was observed that the piece-wise linear approximation method influenced the performance. Based upon these observation it can be stated that as long as visual or numerical quality evaluation is the criteria, bilinear interpolation will provide the most consistent results. However, when considering application of computer algorithm to these images further investigation must be carried out.

REFERENCES

1. J. A. Rowlands, D. M. Hunter, and N. Araj, "X-Ray Imaging Using Amorphous Selenium: A photoinduced discharge readout method for digital mammography", Med. Phys., Vol. 18, pp. 421-431, 1991.
2. V. Swarnakar, M. Jeong, R. Wassermann, E. Andres and D. Wobschall, "Integrated An Integrated Distortion Correction and Reconstruction Technique for Digital Mosaic Mammography", *V. Swarnakar, M. Jeong, R. Wasserman, E. Andres, D. Wobschall,* Proceedings Medical Imaging 97.
3. A. Jalink, J. McAdoo, G. Halama and H. Liu, "CCD Mosaic Technique for Large-Field Digital Mammography", IEEE Trans. on Medical Imaging, Vol. 15, No. 3, June 1996.
4. D. A. Butler and P. K. Person, "A Distortion-Correction Scheme for Industrial Machine-Vision Applications", IEEE Trans. on Robotics and Automation, Vol. 7, No. 4, Aug. 1991 pp. 546-551.
5. R. Salvi, "Introduction to Applied Statistical Signal Analysis", IRWIN 1991.
6. A. K. Jain, "Fundamentals of Digital Image Processing", Prentice Hall 1989.
7. MIAS Database: http://skye.icr.ac.uk/miasdb/miasdb.html.

SESSION 3

Poster Session

Quantifying the limitations of the use of consensus expert committees in ROC studies

Miguel P. Eckstein[a], Thomas D. Wickens[b], Gal Aharanov[a], George Ruan[a], Craig Morioka[a] and James S. Whiting[a]

[a]Department of Medical Physics & Imaging
Cedars Sinai Medical Center
Los Angeles, CA, 90048-1865

[b]Department of Psychology
University of California, Los Angeles

ABSTRACT

Many Receiver Operating Characteristic (ROC) studies rely on establishing "truth" (the gold standard) about lesion absence/presence on the agreement of a panel of experts (consensus expert committees). In addition, in the consensus committee methodology, images where the members of the committee did not reach any agreement about the lesion absence/presence are discarded from the ROC study. But how reliable are "gold standards" established by these expert committees? And does discarding images where no agreement was reached bias the spectrum of difficulty of the test image set for the ROC study? Computer simulated lesions (filling defects) of different strengths (signal contrasts) were embedded in real x-ray coronary angiogram backgrounds in order to measure the agreement among the decisions of members of the committee as a function of signal strength, to establish the accuracy of the decisions of the consensus expert committee and to compare it to individual more inexperienced readers.

Keywords: ROC studies, gold standards, consensus expert committee, assessment of medical image quality

1. INTRODUCTION

A requirement for standard Receiver Operating Characteristic (ROC) studies in medical imaging is knowledge about the lesion presence/absence or abnormality/normality. A common practice is to establish the "truth" about lesion presence or abnormality by an independent and more accurate method (e.g. quantitative image analysis, a different imaging modality, or by biopsy or autopsy methods). When an independent validation analysis is not available, a common method is to use a consensus expert committee to decide on lesion presence and/or abnormality.[1-4] The decisions of the expert committee are then used as a "gold standard" to classify the responses of observers in the ROC study and to exclude from the study those images in which the committee did not agree. Two potential limitations of the expert consensus committee are: 1) Exclusion of images where no agreement is reached by the committee members might bias the spectrum of difficulty in the image samples used for the ROC study. Changes in the spectrum of difficulty in the set of test images in a study might lead to different results when assessing two diagnostic approaches.[5] 2) As other observers, the expert committee might concur in classification errors resulting in a false "gold standard" which might lead to misleading conclusions when assessing diagnostic approaches.

The goals of the present study are to use computer-simulated lesions of three different signal contrasts embedded in real medical image backgrounds: 1) To determine whether selection of cases for a ROC study based on agreement by a consensus expert committee leads to a biased population of signal contrasts in the test-image set. 2) To quantify the classification errors concurred by the consensus expert committee for the different signal contrasts. 3) To compare the performance of the consensus expert committee to that of a second year cardiology fellow and that of an observer with extensive experience in psychophysical studies.

2. METHODS

2.1. Materials

Images were single frames from x-ray coronary angiograms acquired at 30 f/s with a 7" dia. Image intensifier (Advanx/DXC, General Electric Medical Systems). Digital images were obtained with a linear analog amplifier and lookup table to achieve 512x512 image (0.3 mm per pixel) with 256 gray levels. All digital spatial filters were disabled. The signal was a computer-generated hemi-ellipsoid that mimics an arterial filling defect (thrombus). The signal was blurred with a Gaussian point spread function (sd = 1.0 pixels) and combined mathematically with the images with a method that matches the x-ray image generation system.[6] Signals with three different contrasts, high, medium and low were embedded in the angiogram backgrounds. The set of images used in the study were: 60 images with no embedded signals, 20 images with a low contrast signal, 20 images with a medium contrast signal, and 20 images with a high contrast signals. The square root signal contrast energies, SQSCE=sqrt($\Sigma\Sigma$ [s(x,y)/Lo]^2), were 0.681 (low signal contrast), 1.038 (medium signal contrast) and 1.42 (high signal contrast). Images were displayed on a Image Systems ML17 monitor. The mean display luminance of the monitor was 26.6 cd/m^2. The study was conducted in a dark room.

2.2. Observers

The expert consensus committee consisted of three senior cardiologists. The single readers consisted of a second year cardiology fellow and a starting college student with no medical training but with extensive experience working as a psychophysical observer in medical image perception studies.

2.3. Procedure

The study consisted of one reading of all images randomly intermixed. For the consensus committee the procedure was as follows. An image was presented. The experts discussed whether the image contained the lesion. A small pop-up menu was presented with the question: "Is there agreement?" and the two possible answers to be selected ("yes", "no"). If the experts could not reach an agreement on the presence or absence of the lesion they would select "no" and the next image was displayed. If they did agree they would select "yes" and the committee was then instructed to put the cursor and select (with the left button of the mouse) the most probable lesion location (note that they were forced to select a location even if they all agreed that there was no lesion present). After selecting the most probable lesion location, another pop-up menu was presented with the heading "Rate your confidence" followed by 6 possible choices to select from: "high confidence lesion not present", "medium confidence-lesion not present", "low confidence lesion not present", "low confidence lesion present", "medium confidence lesion present", "high confidence lesion present." The experts would then discuss what rating to choose, reach an agreement and select a rating. The next image was then presented. Figure 1 shows a schematic of the procedure.

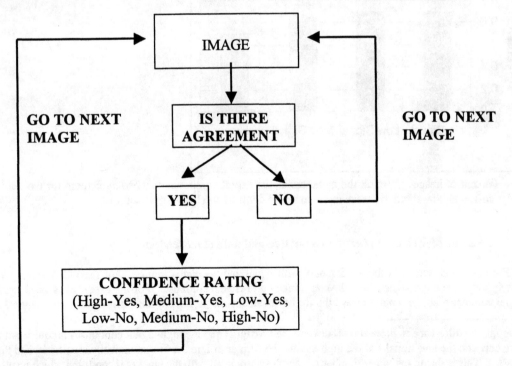

Figure 2. Schematic of the procedure used for the study.

The procedure was basically the same for the individual readers except that the questions related to "agreement within members of the panel" was not included since it was not applicable to a reading by an individual reader.

Prior to starting the actual study, all observers were explained that the lesion was a simulated thrombus, that it would have a fixed size but varying contrast and that each image would or not include only one embedded simulated lesion. About 20 sample images with a high contrast simulated lesion embedded were shown to the observers so they became familiar with the lesion. These sample images were not used in the actual study.

2.4. Data Analysis

The ROC rating data was fit with an equal variance and unequal variance Gaussian model by maximum likelihood. They were 11 estimated parameters: d'_{hc} (detectability of high contrast signal), d'_{mc} (medium contrast) and d'_{lc} (low contrast), as well as the 5 criteria and three variances (in the unequal variance case).

3. RESULTS

3.1. Selection of images by consensus expert committee

From the collected data for the expert committee we can calculate the proportion of images where the committee agreed on lesion presence/absence for each image-group: "no signal", "low contrast signal", "medium contrast signal" and "high contrast signal". Figure 2 shows that the proportion of images in which the expert committee agreed was lowest for the highest signal contrast. Paired z-tests (with pooled variance) for our small sample sizes (n=20 for each of the signal present conditions and n=60 for the signal absent condition) revealed no significant difference ($p < 0.05$) between the high signal and the low-signal and medium signal conditions. However, the difference between the no-signal condition and the high signal condition was significant ($p > 0.05$).[*]

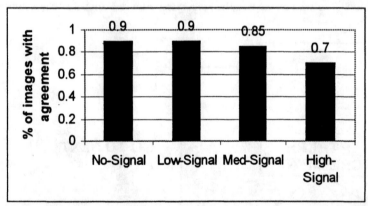

Figure 2. Percent of images in which the members of the expert committee reached agreement for the four signal conditions: no-signal, low-signal contrast, medium signal contrast and high signal contrast.

3.2. ROC parameters for consensus expert committee and individual readers

Ratings were used to fit the ROC model with equal and unequal variance. For the individual readers the ROC was fit only to those images where the committee had reached consensus. For the expert consensus committee the unequal variance model did not improve the fit; however, for the psychophysics trained observer and the 2nd year

---

[*] Even though the difference in proportions between the no-signal and the high-signal conditions is equivalent to the difference between the low-signal and the high-signal, the former difference was statistically significant and the latter was not. This is due to the larger number of samples associated with the no-signal condition which resulted in greater statistical power.

cardiology fellow, the unequal variance model resulted in a better fit. Table 1 shows the index of detectability, d', for the low contrast signal (d'_{lc}), medium contrast signal (d'_{mc}) and high contrast signal (d'_{hc}) for the expert consensus committee, the 2nd year cardiologist and the psychophysics trained observer.[†] The table also shows the decision criteria (λ_1 though λ_5) used to subdivide the confidence ratings. For the highest signal contrast the expert committee did significantly better ($p < 005$) than both individual readers. For the medium signal and low signal contrast conditions we did not find any significant differences between performance for the expert consensus committee and the individual readers ($p > 0.05$). Table 1 shows that the criteria, λ, are larger for the consensus committee suggesting that the consensus committee used a more conservative set of criteria for their decisions.

	Expert Consensus Committee	2nd year cardiology fellow	Psychophysics observer
d'_{lc}	0.585 ± 0.293	0.297 ± 0.272	0.007 ± 0.383
d'_{mc}	0.645 ± 0.299	0.260 ± 0.272	0.602 ± 0.320
d'_{hc}	2.710 ± 0.399	1.156 ± 0.282	1.976 ± 0.393
λ_1	-0.286	-0.528	-1.953
λ_2	0.947	-0.188	-0.442
λ_3	1.157	0.073	0.366
λ_4	1.750	0.465	1.698
λ_5	2.352	1.152	2.490

Table 1. Parameters from ROC fit using maximum likelihood

Figure 3, 4 and 5 show the underlying distributions consistent with the parameters in table 1 for the expert committee (Figure 3), the 2nd year cardiologist (Figure 4) and the psychophysics trained observer (Figure 5). Figure 6 plots the index of detectability, d', for the expert committee and the individual readers for all three signal contrast conditions.

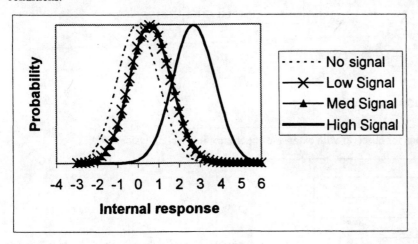

Figure 3. Underlying response distributions for the consensus expert committee

---

[†] For the cases where the unequal variance Gaussian model was used to fit the data, d' was quantified as $d'=\mu/\sqrt{[(0.5(1+\sigma_s^2)]}$ where μ is the distance between the signal and no-signal distributions and σ_s^2 is the variance of the signal distribution.

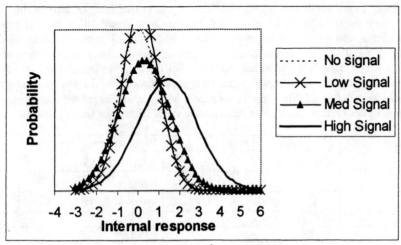

Figure 4. Underlying distributions for 2nd year cardiology fellow

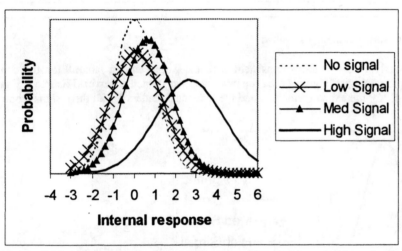

Figure 5. Underlying distributions for observer with extensive experience in psychophysical studies.

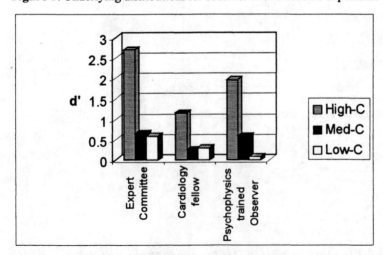

Figure 6. d' for the expert committee , the 2nd year cardiology fellow and the observer with extensive experience in psychophysical experiments.

4. DISCUSSION

4.1. Selection of images by a consensus expert committee.

Our results showed that there was a decrease with increasing signal contrast in the proportion of images in which the consensus expert committee agreed on lesion absence/presence. This seems to be a rather surprising result. Intuition might suggest that the consensus committee should tend to agree more often when the images contain an easily visible signal and disagree more often when the signal is subtle. However, one might also expect the expert committee to agree more often when the signal becomes so subtle that it is seldom detected. In this case, the members of the expert committee would almost always miss the presence of the lesion but concur in their erroneous decision. This seems to be a possible explanation for the medium and low contrast conditions where the expert committee members agreed on their decision but missed most of the lesions. On the other hand, although the signal in the high signal contrast condition is quite visible, it is not visible enough so that the observers correctly detect it on every single occasion. Thus, the high contrast signal condition seemed to be a condition of intermediate difficulty that led to a significant amount of differing decisions by the members of the committee. We believe that if we added an additional condition with an even higher signal contrast, eventually the detection task would become easy enough that the expert committee would concur on lesion presence for every single image.

Our results show that selection of test images for a ROC study based on the agreement of the members of a consensus expert committee lead to a test image set that does not equally represent the categories (signal contrast in our case) from the original set of images. Overall, however the proportion of images for each signal contrast category seems not to be extremely biased towards one signal contrast (Figure 2). However, it is unknown at this point whether the observed bias in the proportion of images for each signal contrast category would result in a significant impact on an assessment of a diagnostic approach.[5]

4.2. ROC studies based on a "gold standard" established by a consensus expert committee

Table 1 and Figure 6 show that performance (d') of the consensus expert committee was very good for the high signal contrast condition but very poor for the low signal contrasts conditions. These results suggest that in the medium and low signal contrast conditions, the committee concurred in erroneous decisions. Therefore, if one established the "gold standard" based on the decisions of the expert committee, one would include 83 % of low contrast signal images with and 76 % of the medium signal contrast images with an erroneous "gold standard" (Figure 7). On the other hand, the problem is not as severe for the no-signal and high signal contrast conditions (Figure 7). Conducting a ROC study with a widely incorrect gold standard might lead to misleading results when evaluating two diagnostic approaches.

The use of an overwhelmingly false "gold standard" will lead to misleading results when assessing diagnostic approaches. For example, an image processing technique that increased the visibility of the signal would lead observers to respond "signal present" more often in the images containing low and medium signal contrast. With a correct "gold standard", these responses would be classified as increasing the true positives. But with our false "gold standard" established by the expert committee, these would be classified as false positives. Thus, the study would conclude that the image processing technique creates artifacts that looked like signals and increased the false positives responses of observers rather than concluding that it improved detectability.

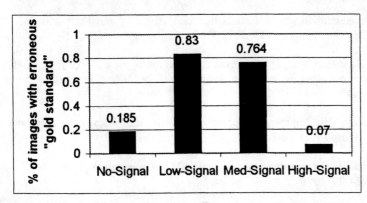

Figure 7. Percentage of images with erroneous "gold standard" established by a consensus expert committee.

4.3. Expert committee vs. individual readers

At the highest signal contrast condition, the expert committee performed better than the individual readers. However, at low signal contrasts the committee did not perform significantly better than the individual observers. We speculate that this dichotomy in results is due to the effects of signal position uncertainty inherent in the task. Surprisingly, the psychophysics trained observer outperformed the 2nd year cardiologists. We hypothesize that the psychophysics trained observer has had actually more experience detecting these types of lesions than a 2nd year cardiology fellow. A close look at the decision criteria, suggests that the expert committee seemed to act more conservatively about calling lesion presence, than the 2nd year cardiology fellow and the psychophysics trained observer.

5. CONCLUSIONS

Our results suggest that when a consensus expert committee is the only available method to establish truth about lesion presence/absence, alternative methods should be used to evaluate diagnostic accuracy of low contrast signals. Two possible options are the use of computer simulated signals[6,7,8] and/or alternative analysis methods that assume no "gold standard" - mixture distributions.[9,10]

6. ACKNOWLEDGEMENTS

This was work was supported by National Institute of Health (NIH) grants RO1 HL53455.

7. REFERENCES

1. Steckel R.J., Batra P., Johnson S., Zucker M., Sayre J., Goldin J., Lee M., Patel M., Morrison H., Chest teleradiology in a teaching hospital emergency practice, American Journal of Roentgenology, 1997 Jun, 168(6):1409-13.

2. Richmond B.J., Powers C., Piraino D.W., Freed H., Meziane M.A., Hale J.C., Schluchter M.D., Schils J., Gragg L.A., Diagnostic efficacy of digitized images vs. plain films: a study of the joints of the fingers, American Journal of Roentgenology, 158(2):437-41, 1992

3. Scarfe W.C., Langlais R.P., Nummikoski P., Dove S.B., McDavid W.D., Deahl S.T., Yuan C.H., Clinical comparison of two panoramic modalities and posterior bite-wing radiography in the detection of proximal dental caries, Oral Surgery, Oral Medicine, and Oral Pathology, 1994 Feb, 77(2):195-207, 1994

4. Wilson A.J., Mann F.A., Murphy W.A. Jr, Monsees B.S., Linn M.R., Photostimulable phosphor digital radiography of the extremities: diagnostic accuracy compared with conventional radiography, Amreican Journal of Roentgenology, 157(3):533-8, 1991

5. Swets, J.A, Getty, D.J., Pickett, R.M., D'orsi, C.J., Seltzer, S.E., McNeil, B.J., Enhancing and evaluating diagnostic accuracy, Med. Dec. Making, 11:9-18, 1991

6. Eckstein, M.P., Whiting, J.S.,Visual signal detection in structured backgrounds I: Effect of signal contrasts and number of possible locations, Journal of the Opt. Soc. of Am. A 13, 1777-1787, 1996

7. Eckstein, M.P., Morioka, C.A., Whiting, J.S., Eigler, N.L., Psychophysical evaluation of the effect of JPEG, full-frame and wavelet image compression on signal detectability in medical image noise," in Medical Imaging 1995: Image Perception, H. Kundel, ed., Proc. SPIE 2436, 79-89, 1995

8. Eigler N.L, Eckstein, M.P., Honig, D., Whiting, J.S., Improving detection of coronary morphologic features from digital angiograms: effect of stenosis stabilized display," Circulation 89, 2700-2709, 1994

9. Henkelman R.M., Kay I., Bronskill M.J., Receiver operator characteristic (ROC) analysis without truth [see comments], Medical Decision Making, 10(1):24-29, 1990

10. Kundel H.L., Polansky M., Mixture distribution and receiver operating characteristic analysis of bedside chest imaging with screen-film and computed radiography, academic Radiology, 4(1):1-7, 1997

Computerized interpretation of solitary pulmonary nodules

Hideo Suzuki[a], Hirotsugu Takabatake[b], Masaki Mori[c],

Masanobu Mitani[d], and Hiroshi Natori[d]

[a]IBM Japan,   Nihonbashi Hakozaki-Cho, Tokyo Japan 1038510

[b]Minamiichijou Hospital

[c]Sapporo Kousei Hospital

[d]Sapporo Medical Univ., Sapporo

ABSTRACT

In physicians' interpretation, morphologic characteristics of pulmonary nodules are not only important signs for the discrimination, but also important features for the diagnosis with a reasonable degree of confidence. This paper describes about the computerized interpretation system which is developed to analyze the relation between the measuring values and the morphologic characteristics, and to make clear the logic of physicians' diagnosis.

We think that the four basic morphologic characteristics of the discriminative diagnosis between benign and malignant nodules exist which are: 1.the density; 2.the homogeneity; 3.the definition; and 4.the convergence. To obtain each grade of the parameters, we developed an interpretation system. On the other hand, to obtain digital feature values, we used our computer aided diagnosis (CAD) system.

Interpretation experiments were performed by using 15 benign and 19 malignant cases of chest X-ray CT images. As the result of a statistical analysis, some digital features have the significant differences between benign and malignant nodules, and the morphologic characteristics have also differences. Therefore the computerized system is feasible to help physicians' interpretation to distinct between malignant and benign nodules by showing digital feature values as some references.

Keywords: computerized interpretation, malignant nodules, digital feature values, morphologic characteristics, discriminative diagnosis

1.INTRODUCTION

Distinction between benign and malignant pulmonary nodules is a common clinical problem. We think morphologic characteristics of pulmonary nodules are important signs in physicians' interpretation. Further, it is known that various measuring values on digital images like a circularity factor are related to the morphologic characteristics. Therefore we think digital feature values have some relations with physicians' interpretations, and are able to help their discriminative diagnosis between benign and malignant nodules. To obtain the feature values, we used our computer aided diagnosis(CAD) system, which was developed for detecting pulmonary nodules and diagnosis lung cancer automatically. The feature values in the CAD system are: 1. a mean density value; 2. a circularity factor; and 3. an entropy of densities/

density differences. This paper describes the method to analyze the relation between the feature values and the morphologic characteristics, and to make clear the logic of physicians' diagnosis.[1-5]

2.MATERIALS

About subjects of this study, we collected 15 cases of benign tumor, and 19 cases of malignant tumor. The benign cases consist of several diseases like tuberculosis, and each of the malignant cases contains a pathologically proven adenocarcinoma (one type of lung cancer). As for the average measuring values are:

	Area(mm^2)	Max. diameter(mm)	Min. diameter(mm)
Benign(15 cases)	180	17.6	12.9
Malignant(19 cases)	229	17.5	14.1

3.IMAGING PROTOCOL

Spiral CT was performed with a X-Vision unit (Toshiba medical systems co.ltd. Tokyo, JAPAN) at 230mAs and 130kV. During scanning, patients were instructed to hold their breath at functional residual capacity level. Collimation width was set to 5mm by using 360 degree linear interpolation algorithm and a matrix size of 512x512 pixels. Intravenous contrast media was not administered. All images were viewed at lung and mediastinal window settings but were filmed only at lung window settings (width, 1600 HU; center, -600 HU).

4.METHOD

Each CT image (512x512x12bit) was converted to 512x512x8bit image by means of linear transformation. When the center of a tumor (benign or malignant) was extracted by a physician manually, each feature value was calculated by the system automatically. An interpretation experiment was also performed by the physician on each image.

To obtain the feature value, we used our computer aided diagnosis system, which was developed for lung cancer diagnosis. The system can detect lung cancer candidates and discriminate whether each candidate is a lung cancer or a false-positive. The filter to detect lung cancer candidates is named "Directional Contrast Filter for Nodule:DCF-N," and has high sensitivity to malignant nodules. The system also has a function of discriminative diagnosis, which includes a function for measuring feature values. As a result of the system to more than 200 cases, we obtained a consistent figure of over 80% accuracy. Therefore, we consider that the function of measuring with the system is effective to discriminate between benign and malignant nodules for CT images.

Fig.1 shows the widow used for calculating the feature values. The window consists of five concentric circles whose radii are r, 2r, 3r, 4r, 5r, respectively. The 'r' is calculated by using each value of area, automatically. Therefore it consists of one circle and four annular regions. In each region, two defined features, the mean density and the circularity factor, are calculated on the original and the DCF-N output image. Then 20 feature values are obtained according to the following equation:

5(regions) x 2(features) x 2(images) = 20

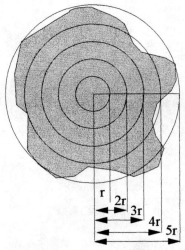

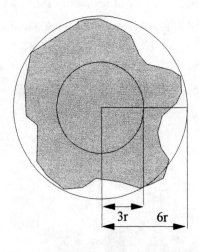

Fig. 1 Window for calculating mean density and
Circularity factor.

Fig. 2 Window for calculating entropies.

Fig.2 shows the widow used for calculating the feature values(entropies). The window consists of two concentric circles whose radii are 3r and 6r. It consists of one circle and one annular region. In each region, two defined features, the entropy of the densities and the entropy of the density differences, are calculated on the original, the DCF-N output image and a different filtered image. The filter is named "Directional Contrast Filter for Vessel:DCF-V," and has high sensitivity to blood vessels. Then 12 feature values are obtained according to the following equation:

2(regions) x 2(features) x 3(images) = 12

To obtain a grade of four morphologic characteristics and a grade of malignant, we develop a system of computerized interpretation. Fig. 3 shows a screen of input in the system. By using the system, physicians are able to input

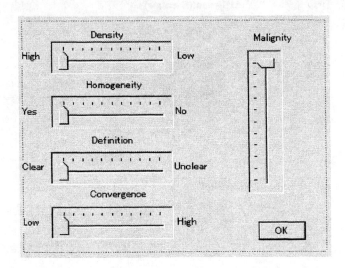

Fig.3 The input window in the interpretaion sytem.
Physicians can see the object image, can input
a grade of 0-10 levels in each item by moving
the slider. Smaller grade shows the feature of
benign.

the grade in each character of nodules as their own definitions, and the grade of the discrimination between benign and malignant nodules. Fig. 4 shows examples of the interpretation.

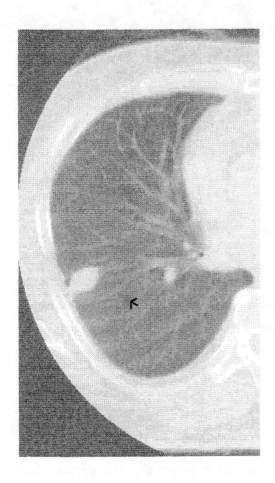

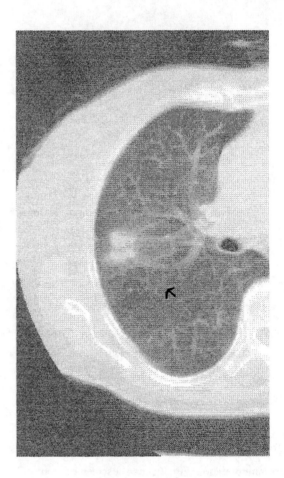

Benign(Example)

Malignant(Example)

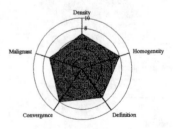

Fig.4 Examples of the interpretaion sytem.
The left side shows a case of benign. The right side shows a case of malignant.
Each rader chart shows the result of input grades.

5.RESULT

As for the feature values which were calculated by the CAD system, four feature values have significant differences between benign and malignant nodules as follows:

(1) The mean density value at the innermost region on the original image.

(2) The circularity factor at the innermost region on the original image data.

(3) The entropy of the densities on the DCF-V output image data.

(4) The entropy of the density differences on the DCF-V output image data.

As for the interpretation system, there are also significant differences in morphologic features (Fig.5).

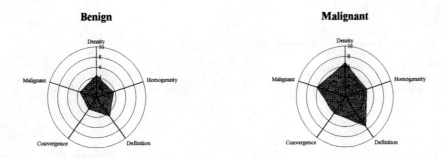

Fig.5 The result of the interpretation experiment

Each radar chart shows the average of the input data.

Benign : 15 cases

Malignant : 19 cases

6.DISCUSSION

We consider that each feature value by the CAD system is related to the morphologic characteristics by the physician. Especially the entropy value of the density differences on the DCF-V output image is strongly related to the convergence in the morphologic characteristics. To make clear the relations of the features from the system and the physicians, the further experiment to a number of the physicians by means of the computerized interpretation system is required.

As for the interpretation experiment, however both shapes of the two radar charts are similar (Fig.5), the physician can easily distinct between benign and malignant cases by using the morphologic characteristics. This means that the grade of each morphologic characteristic is important to discrimination. Therefore both the computerized interpretation system and the CAD system are effective to discriminative diagnosis between benign and malignant. These systems are also useful for training residents in describing morphologic characteristics with minimum observers variation.

7.REFERENCES

1. M.Mori, et.al., "Computerized Supporting System for Detection of Pulmonary Nodules," Supplement to Radiology, vol.169(P), p.447, Nov.1988.

2. H.Takabatake, et.al., "Computer-aided Detection of Pulmonary Nodules on Chest Radiographs," Supplement to Radiology, vol.173(P), p.455, Nov.1989.

3. H.Suzuki, et.al., "An experimental system for detecting lung tumors by chest x-ray image processing," Proc. of SPIE, vol.1450, pp.90-107, Feb.1991.

4. H.Suzuki, et.al., "Development of a Computer-Aided Detection System for Lung Cancer Diagnosis," Proc. of SPIE, vol.1652, pp.567-571, Feb.1992.

5. H.Suzuki, et.al., "Computer-aided diagnosis system for lung tumors," Proc. of SPIE, vol.2710, pp.1035-1038, Feb.1996.

Further author information –

Hideo Suzuki: Email: HSZK@jp.ibm.com; Telephone: 81-3-3808-4447; Fax: 81-3-3664-4796